Amanita Muscaria Microdosing

Complete Guide to Microdosing With Fly Agaric for Mind and Body Healing

Inspirational Creator

from various sources. Please consult a licensed professional before attempting any techniques outlined in this book.

By reading this document, the reader agrees that under no circumstances is the author responsible for any losses, direct or indirect, that are incurred as a result of the use of the information contained within this document, including, but not limited to, errors, omissions, or inaccuracies.

ISBN 978-1-922940-032 (E-book)

ISBN 978-1-922940-056 (Paperback)

Cover Design by Andav

Published by Inspirational Creator

Bil Harret & Anastasia V. Sasha

First Edition (2022)

Table of Contents

Introduction

Fly agaric is believed to have gotten its name from an old European practice. This mushroom was crushed, dipped, or sprinkled in milk or sugar, and then used as an insecticide, specifically against flies. Also known as *Amanita muscaria*, it has become the most emblematic mushroom, with its distinguished aspect and red-and-white coloring. This mushroom appears in artwork dating back about as far back as there is art to be dated. You may even recognize it as the mushroom normally seen in popular media like the *Super Mario Brothers*, *Alice in Wonderland*, or even the fairytales that you grew up with.

Typically, *Amanita muscaria* is classified as a poisonous or hallucinogenic mushroom, especially in mushroom field guides. While this fungus does have psychoactive properties, when prepared correctly, administered safely, and taken in the correct dosage, it can provide you with a number of health benefits. Think of it this way. You wouldn't take more than the recommended dosage of paracetamol for your headache because you understand that it could involve adverse side effects. This same concept is applied to fly agaric.

Amanita muscaria is a versatile species of mushroom; as such, its benefits include its ability to treat anxiety, act as a painkiller and anti-inflammatory, treat depression, and improve intestinal cramps and constipation. It has also been used to reduce allergy symptoms, treat addictions, migraine, insomnia, epilepsy, autism, menopause in women, sore throats, and musculoskeletal pains, including arthritis and neuropathic pains. Other daily or work-related benefits that have been reported include—but are not limited to—calmness, creativity, higher energy levels, physical stamina, improved mood, increased relational skills, concentration, and mental clarity. Unfortunately, while this mushroom has many potential benefits, there are very few scientific and controlled-scale studies that have been conducted regarding its medicinal properties.

In this guide, I aim to provide you with an overview of *Amanita muscaria* using the current knowledge available regarding its health benefits. As someone who has suffered from polyarthritis since a young age, with similar symptoms to those of rheumatoid arthritis, I have tried a number of different medications, but my pain remains with me 24-7. Like so many other individuals who experience chronic pain, I looked for alternative remedies that could both relieve my pain and improve my health. My research took me to Amanita muscaria. After an in-depth investigation, I was able to determine that this mushroom had the potential to be my healer somehow.

If you are looking to improve your own symptoms of chronic pain or illness, health, and well-being, or simply want to improve your overall health using an alternative remedy, then use the information contained in this guide to decide for yourself whether it's something that you want to pursue.

I will provide you with an overview of *Amanita muscaria*, its nature, and its composition, as well as its potential health benefits to help you decide if it fits your lifestyle. I'm going to take you by the hand and explain every step you need to identify it without mistaking it, prepare it correctly, and use it safely. Additionally, I will provide you with a brief explanation of the possible risks of pursuing this mushroom as an alternative remedy.

While using this mushroom to improve your own health can involve some risks—especially when prepared incorrectly, used irresponsibly, or taken in the wrong dosage—it won't hurt you to learn more about its potential benefits. You can then use that knowledge to help you make an informed decision. If you are prepared to open your mind and learn about the unique qualities of *Amanita muscaria*, then turn the page and get ready to start your journey.

Chapter 1: Microdosing With Amanita Muscaria

Those of us investigating this unique mushroom and its beneficial properties are often called pioneers, as there is almost no clinical research or medical data related to the intake of very small doses of *Amanita muscaria*. But that doesn't mean that there is no information available at all. Anecdotal evidence has provided us with the foundation needed to begin researching the uses and benefits of fly agaric in small doses. This evidence comes from thousands upon thousands of consistent data reports.

Despite this evidence, mushroom field guides often classify *Amanita muscaria* as toxic due to its chemical components and the need for careful preparation. Fortunately, modern medicine has advanced enough that proper medical treatment can help you recover, should you experience any adverse effects from the ingestion of fly agaric; however, while fatalities are rare, the risk is still present. Gaining an understanding of how this mushroom works can help you learn how to use it safely and lower your risk of adverse effects. Through proper preparation and administration of the correct dosage, you can use *Amanita muscaria* safely. Take the time to read through the information provided in this chapter carefully and start building the foundation needed for safely using and ingesting this mushroom. I will start this process by discussing the different types of information and sources available to us.

Anecdotal Versus Empirical Evidence

Amanita muscaria is found mainly in the northern hemisphere. This mushroom is commonly found in Northern Europe and North America, as it can grow on the pine and birch trees that grow, specifically in these climates. The relationship between *Amanita muscaria* and these trees is symbiotic. Essentially, this mushroom and the trees it grows beneath have an interdependent relationship. This may explain why the majority of the information that we do have regarding *Amanita muscaria's* uses and properties originates from Siberia, whose people have been harvesting and ingesting this mushroom safely for many, many years. This region also provided us with evidence of this mushroom being used in folk medicine. As a result, two different types of evidence emerged when studying *Amanita muscaria's* applications and benefits: anecdotal and empirical evidence.

Anecdotal Evidence

Stories passed down from our ancestors, trip reports, and testimonials from individuals who have been practicing microdosing using *Amanita muscaria* form the majority of the information that we currently have regarding this mushroom and its properties. This type of information is known as *anecdotal evidence*. Fortunately, more research has been conducted in recent years regarding the properties and benefits of fly agaric in terms of improving your health, but this research has been hindered due to various factors, such as costs.

An Example of Anecdotal Evidence

Baba Masha—a researcher and physician—conducted an interesting international project through Telegram to collect public-opinion data and anecdotal evidence of how more than 3,000 individuals experienced positive outcomes after safely microdosing with *Amanita muscaria*. I have a great deal of respect for Dr. Masha, as she worked hard and committed to conducting research on a topic with little to no proven scientific data to assist her and only anecdotal evidence to guide her.

In Baba Masha's book—*Microdosing with Amanita Muscaria: Creativity, Healing, and Recovery With the Sacred Mushroom*—she dedicated more than two-thirds of the book's length to solely discussing the reports and consistent data that she received from her study. This study revealed that *Amanita muscaria* microdosing can improve your mood, manage and relieve symptoms of asthenia and depression, provide you with energy, or even calm you down depending on the time of day that you take your dosage. Subscribers (the individuals who took part in her study) also claimed pain-relief properties and positive effects in different somatic diseases. *Amanita muscaria* can also be used to improve the quality of a person's sleep.

Empirical Evidence

As mentioned, there are no controlled and documented comprehensive scale studies on the medicinal effects of *Amanita muscaria* in modern, international pharmacology or medicine. However, there are a number of studies that have provided insight into the medicinal properties of fly agaric components. While *Amanita muscaria* has been scarcely researched, there are a number of studies that have been conducted on its medical properties.

Examples of Empirical Evidence

A study was conducted on the effect of muscimol on Parkinson's disease. It was found that when injected into the subthalamic nucleus, the tremors normally associated with this disease were suppressed. This demonstrated that muscimol injections had the potential ability to reverse Parkinson's symptoms (Pahapill et al., 1999; Levy, 2001).

The effect of ibotenic acid and muscimol was also studied in relation to its impact on neurological disorders—like Huntington's disease—and epilepsy. The study revealed that muscimol was involved in the process of making anticonvulsants—like gabatril (tiagabine). The results of this study led to muscimol being advertised as a possible therapeutic agent in the treatment of epilepsy (Krogsgaard-Larsen et al., 1977; Krogsgaard-Larsen et al., 1996; Krogsgaard-Larsen et al., 2004; and Tamminga et al., 1978).

What Does This Mean for You?

Excluding Dr. Masha's research study, the information normally provided during other studies is quite limited in terms of *Amanita muscaria*. While Dr. Masha's study is considered a great example of anecdotal evidence, many of the experiments that *have* been conducted to gather empirical evidence were mainly performed on animals (normally rats) or *in vitro* (experiments conducted in glass test tubes, petri dishes, and other

15

glass vessels in a laboratory). As such, the information regarding the effects, benefits, and safety of *Amanita muscaria*—in terms of human use and consumption—is limited.

Nevertheless, the studies and evidence that does exist provide us with useful knowledge that can support the information received from anecdotal evidence. For example, treatments involving the administration of muscimol (a constituent of *Amanita muscaria*) may have the ability to alleviate Parkinson's symptoms, provide neuroprotective effects (*in vitro*), assist in the treatment of Huntington's disease, chronic schizophrenia, epilepsy, and reduce anxiety levels. Hydroxypyrrollidone (another chemical component) may have antibiotic and antifungal benefits, while gaboxadol may be able to promote better sleep. Additionally, fucomannogalactan and glucan have the potential to inhibit inflammatory pain (*Amanita muscaria*, Matsumoto et al. 1969).

There may not be a lot of empirical evidence regarding the use and benefits of *Amanita muscaria*, but the information and anecdotal evidence that *is* available to us provides valuable insight into *how* to use this mushroom safely, in a way that can improve your physical health and well-being. However, you need to learn about the basic science behind the main components of fly agaric to help you understand what makes this mushroom dangerous and why, as well as how you can use techniques like decarboxylation to make the ingestion of *Amanita muscaria* safer.

Pharmacological Overview

Amanita muscaria is made up of a number of complex chemicals. Gaining a better understanding of what these chemicals are and how they affect your body is the key to understanding how to use this mushroom safely. The main chemicals that I will focus on are ibotenic acid, muscimol, muscarine, and muscazone. These chemicals are the most studied compounds found in fly agaric. I will be focusing mainly on two primary compounds: ibotenic acid and muscimol.

Ibotenic Acid

Concentrated mainly in the caps of the *Amanita muscaria* mushroom, this neurotoxic compound becomes harmful if it builds up in our system when any dose larger than what our digestive tract can normally metabolize is ingested. The psychoactive properties of this acid can also result in adverse effects like poisoning. Ibotenic acid is found in large quantities in the fresh, raw *Amanita muscaria* mushroom. Through techniques like decarboxylation, this neurotoxic acid can be converted into muscimol—a safer, psychotropic compound with a variety of benefits when correctly administered—before being consumed.

Ibotenic acid has the ability to activate NMDA receptors. These receptors play an important role in regulating various neurological functions in your body, including your brain's capacity for neuroplasticity, breathing, the formation of memories, learning, and locomotion. This acid has the ability to trigger your body's glutamate receptors (receptors responsible for controlling your neuronal activity). The activation of these receptors can result in large amounts of calcium entering your cells, resulting in a neurotoxic effect. Surrounding tissue damage might also occur, according to some researchers once reactive oxygen species are triggered. But this last fact is controversial because the evidence is based on introducing ibotenic acid DIRECTLY into the brain of the animals of the experiment, resulting in brain damage. Dizocilpine can block ibotenic acid neurotoxicity. Additionally, the effects of such interactions due to the presence of ibotenic acid in your body are believed to be the cause of the psychoactive effects that normally occur when you are intoxicated.

Muscimol

Also known as "pantherine" or "agarin," muscimol is metabolized by transamination and is one of the principal constituents of *Amanita muscaria*. This salt may also have the ability to permeate your body's blood-brain barrier, but this has yet to be studied in depth. Ten times more potent than ibotenic acid, muscimol is a neurologically potent and selective agonist of the gamma-aminobutyric acid (GABA-A) receptors. These receptors have the ability to block certain signals in the brain and spinal cord, slowing the brain down and exerting a controlling effect over hyperactive cells that are associated with conditions such as stress, fear, and anxiety. As such, muscimol displays sedative-hypnotic, depressant, and hallucinogenic psychoactivity. It also possesses analgesic properties, with recent studies showing promise in treating specific conditions associated (Tsujikawa et al., 2006).

When focusing on using *Amanita muscaria* for improving your health and well-being, muscimol is the substance that you want to focus on. It is found in very small amounts in the fresh, raw mushroom; however, through processes such as decarboxylation, you can convert the ibotenic acid into muscimol. In general, muscimol promotes calmness, relaxation, and improved sleep.

What Are the Ratios of Ibotenic Acid to Muscimol?

Typically, the ibotenic acid to muscimol ratio of *Amanita muscaria*'s fungal cap tissue would be 9:1 or greater in fresh samples. However, the ratio of the ibotenic acid to muscimol will decrease through processes such as drying. A common ibotenic acid to muscimol ratio would be 3:2 in dried specimens (Google Patents, 2013).

Muscarine

A toxic substance found only in small, harmless trace amounts in *Amanita muscaria*; as such, you would need to ingest a large amount of this specific toxin (which adds up to numerous fly agaric mushrooms) before you will start being affected *specifically* by this toxin. Generally, this substance can stimulate your body's *smooth muscles*—these are muscles found in your internal organs—triggering involuntary contractions, resulting in effects such as diarrhea, abdominal pain, increased salivation, and vomiting.

Muscazone

Formed by the breakdown of ibotenic acid through exposure to ultraviolet radiation (UV), this chemical can be found in the European specimens of *Amanita muscaria*. Muscazone has a small impact on your body and its effects include memory loss, visual damage, and mental confusion.

While *Amanita muscaria* contains a number of substances, little is known about their exact effects on the mind and body due to a lack of empirical research. When studying fly agaric; however, our focus is mainly on ibotenic acid, muscimol, muscarine, and muscazone as their roles are important for effectively using this mushroom to improve your health and well-being safely.

Additionally, the elemental distribution in a specific geographic zone is variable and may change according to soil properties, climate, time, mode of harvesting, preparation, and even storage.

Toxicology

From the section above, you should now understand that if *Amanita muscaria* is incorrectly handled, prepared, and ingested, it can lead to adverse effects, increasing your risk of being poisoned. Please remember that each *Amanita muscaria* mushroom will contain different chemical concentrations, regardless of their size. This means that the amount and ratio of the chemical compounds found in each mushroom will vary according to the season and region in which they are being harvested, their maturity, height, and other factors.

In addition, the active constituents of fly agaric can be dissolved in water. As such, practicing the correct preparation techniques can detoxify the mushroom and make it edible. For example, mushroom caps can be boiled in water—for a specific period—before being prepared for traditional consumption. After being boiled, the water must be discarded to get rid of, in this case, the active constituents found in the mushroom, allowing for partial detoxification. Then, most people will fry or pickle them.

Drying *Amanita muscaria* is an effective method for converting ibotenic acid to muscimol. I will provide you with more in-depth information regarding the correct preparation of fly agaric for consumption in chapters 2 and 5.

Please note that the onset of the symptoms of *Amanita muscaria* poisoning is rapid after significant exposure. Significant exposure means that you consumed the fly agaric raw or in high doses. If you start experiencing adverse side effects within half an hour to one and a half hours after ingestion—or you suspect that you have *Amanita muscaria* poisoning—please seek emergency medical attention. A study of several poisoning cases, in which higher doses of *Amanita muscaria* were consumed to evoke hallucinations, showed that the individuals were able to recover with no damage to their organs (Satora et al., 2005). While you are aware that consumption of this mushroom can be risky, you may be wondering what the best method for detoxification is.

Detoxification Using Decarboxylation

Decarboxylation is a process whereby heat is applied to the *Amanita muscaria* mushroom for a specific period (depending on how you prepare the mushroom) in order to remove the carboxyl from the molecule. Through this process, the risk normally associated with ibotenic acid is lowered as it is converted into muscimol.

According to Tsonuda et al. (1993), through the use of high heat—for a longer period—the ibotenic acid present in *Amanita muscaria* is converted to muscimol. This decreases the potency of the ibotenic acid as it is converted into muscimol, which increases. This can also be applied vice versa. Lower heat means less ibotenic acid is converted. However, the final amount of ibotenic acid converted will also depend on the type of detoxification method being used, and the unique chemical makeup of the mushroom itself. By removing the moisture from the fly agaric as quickly as possible—through the application of heat—the potency of the mushroom will be protected (Tsonuda et al., 1993; Buschfunkistan, 2019).

A Brief Overview of Amanita Muscaria's Effects

While Chapter 4 will discuss the common side effects of using *Amanita muscaria* in detail, it's important that you remember that its effects can be unpredictable. The presence of each compound found in a single *Amanita muscaria* mushroom will depend on the habitat they were grown in, the season, height, the method of harvesting and storing, as well as how you prepare them. In general, there are a number of different side effects that you could experience, including mild nausea, vomiting, low blood pressure, drowsiness, euphoria, relaxation, mood changes, and a loss of balance.

You also need to be aware that an identical dose of the same mushroom, or batch, will have highly variable effects and result in unique reactions in two individuals of the same gender and body weight. There is no fixed statement that can be made regarding dosage. Although there is a typical intake range for microdosing, it will mostly depend on the person's sensitivity to the substance and will be calculated, empirically, starting low.

Each *Amanita muscaria* mushroom is different but having a basic understanding of its pharmacology and toxicology will help you better understand the risks and benefits of using this mushroom to improve your health and well-being. This will allow you to make an informed decision when deciding whether to pursue this mushroom for improving your health. While the information contained here is as up-to-date and as accurate as possible, don't be afraid to seek out new information as new research studies may emerge that provide more detail as to how *Amanita muscaria* can be used safely to benefit your overall well-being.

Key Takeaways

- There is a larger amount of anecdotal evidence on the benefits of *Amanita muscaria* compared to empirical evidence.

- The mushroom is made up of a number of complex chemicals, including ibotenic acid, muscimol, muscarine, and muscazone.

- Our focus is mainly on the conversion of the neurotoxin ibotenic acid to the more beneficial muscimol.

- The chemical composition of two *Amanita muscaria* mushrooms will never be identical.

- Incorrect handling, preparation, and dosage of the mushroom can increase your risk of poisoning.

- Decarboxylation is a popular method for converting ibotenic acid to muscimol.

- The effect of *Amanita muscaria* on your body can be unpredictable.

Learning about the toxins found in *Amanita muscaria* can help you understand the importance of the correct handling and preparation of this mushroom. Additionally, it emphasizes why you can't eat the mushroom raw. This information provides you with the foundation needed to start learning how to microdose with *Amanita muscaria* safely in Chapter 2.

If you are enjoying this book so far, it would mean a lot to me if you could take a minute to review or rate it on the respective platform you acquired it from. Did you know that just 0.5 - 1% of readers do actually end up leaving a review? I have to admit that I used to not be that 1%, but now I do it different since I know how meaningful this can be to independent writers.

Chapter 2: All You Need to Know Before Starting Microdosing

Microdosing has become more well-known, and even popular, in recent years. The practice of taking a small dosage of a substance—that normally has psychedelic properties—can help a person enjoy its more beneficial properties, in terms of their mental and physical health, without having to experience the effects that would normally impair their regular functioning. You may already know what microdosing is, or you may not. This chapter aims to provide you with an overview of what this practice entails when choosing to use *Amanita muscaria* for improving your health and well-being, including how you can determine your optimal microdose and the different forms that fly agaric can be used in.

How to Find Your Optimal Microdose

Microdosing does not have a universal dosage; instead, the recommended dosages are often based on testimonials of what worked for a group of individuals. But that doesn't mean that the recommended dosage is the right one for you. Not only does the concentration of chemicals in each *Amanita muscaria* cap differ, but every person reacts differently to the same dosage. A number of factors can influence your reaction to a dosage, including your weight, gender, sensitivity to the compounds in fly agaric, and even your predisposition to mental health issues such as anxiety and depression. A person's individual sensitivity to the effects of *Amanita muscaria* always has to be taken into consideration when practicing microdosing, which is why many resources regarding this practice will tell you to "start small!" As such, it is best to start out with the smallest dosage and then slowly increase or decrease it to get the desired benefits.

Additionally, the form that *Amanita muscaria* is consumed in will also influence how it affects you, even if it comes from the same batch of mushrooms. As such, the dosage recommendations that I make in this chapter are not fixed or universal.

What Does Anecdotal Research Say?

In Baba Masha's study, she evaluated the effects of *Amanita muscaria* microdosing in its different forms. It was found that in over 1,000 participants involved in the study, 92% of the individuals experienced positive effects after microdosing with *Amanita muscaria*, while 2% of the participants experienced negative results. Her results showed that no discomfort (such as nausea) was experienced by 57% of the participants, while 34% experienced discomfort when they used freshly dried

Amanita muscaria, and only 9% with the cured (fermented) fly agaric. After the dosage course had been completed, 74% of the participants reported stable effects, and 21% only during the reception with no dependency.

Amanita muscaria microdosing can have a number of benefits for your well-being. According to the reports, when participants took their dose in the evening, they reported falling asleep quicker and experiencing improved rest.

Those who took it in the morning reported an improvement in their overall well-being, allowing them to experience a more positive mood and attitude, increased energy levels, improved social skills, a boost in their creativity, and they felt calmer, to name a few.

Dr. Masha found that microdosing for up to a month and then taking a 10-day break was the best dosage schedule for the reception of *Amanita muscaria.* The test subject—or host—could then use the interruption to determine the dose's efficacy and the stability of the treatment. Their determination would help them decide further microdosing, and whether to increase or decrease their intake. This break could also be used to help them determine the dose's effectiveness and stability.

The study revealed that many of the project participants found that the cumulative effects of microdosing, and the effect of continuing this practice, remained with them after a week.

Determining Your Optimal Dosage

While everyone reacts differently to the same *Amanita muscaria* microdose, you can use the recommended dosage to determine your personal optimal dosage. But first, you need to understand that an optimal dosage will not cause changes in your behavior, perception, or consciousness. If you experience increased salivation, strong nausea, euphoria, hallucinations, fractals, sadness, weakness, dizziness, insomnia, or irritability, among others, then you know that your current dosage needs to be lowered. The optimal *Amanita muscaria* microdose—in terms of the results of thousands of individual reports—is 0,5 to 2 g (0.02 to 0.07 oz) of the dried fungus.

This measurement is considered the optimal dosage according to the reports, but you have to remember that your optimal dosage will depend on your unique reaction, the potency of the current batch of *Amanita muscaria* that you are using, as well as the form of consumption.

My Microdosing Experience Using Amanita Muscaria

Personally, I would recommend that you start with a dosage of 0.5 g (about 0,02 oz) of dried *Amanita muscaria* in the morning—while fasting (fasting aids effective absorption) as you may experience nausea in the beginning—and depending on the effect, increase or lower your next dosage. Some people, like me, take the dosage twice a day by splitting a single dose into two doses, while others take it only a few times a week.

I am currently taking capsules with dry cap *Amanita muscaria* powder of 0,01 oz (0,3 g) in the morning, and 0,01 oz (0,6 g) in the evening. At night, I use the second powdered dosage to make a tea that is heated to about 150 to 194°F (65 to 90°C) for around 30 minutes. The heat increases the level of muscimol in the fly agaric powder through decarboxylation. Muscimol acts as a relaxant that allows me to sleep better.

After the 30 minutes is up, I allow the tea some time to cool so that the powdered *Amanita muscaria* can sink to the bottom of the container, making it easier to discard. Please remember that the powder **has** to be discarded before the tea is drunk (according to your correctly measured dosage). Drinking the tea at night is key for me because it prevents my pain from waking me up, or at least not as much if I had not taken the tea. Improved sleep is vital to me, as it has the ability to help reduce the inflammation and pain associated with polyarthritis.

Using the information in this section as a guide, you can now work out your optimal dosage of *Amanita muscaria*, as well as what your dosage schedule would look like. I would recommend that you first read through the entire book to ensure that you have all the information you need. You may even find that your dosage, and the form in which you administer it, will change depending on what you feel comfortable with and what works best for you.

The Importance of Decarboxylation

In this section, I will discuss why decarboxylation is so important to the microdosing process. Decarboxylation places an emphasis on converting the neurotoxic ibotenic acid into the safer, more beneficial muscimol—which is normally found in very small amounts in the fresh, raw *Amanita muscaria* mushroom. While various decarboxylation methods exist, many of the ones studied—in terms of the effect of this conversion process on fly agaric—require specialized equipment and chemicals that can only be found in a laboratory. This makes it difficult to replicate safely at home. But that doesn't mean it's impossible.

Warning: A variety of *Amanita muscaria* decarboxylation methods exist that can be practiced at home. However, you have to be extremely cautious when using these methods, as you do not have the equipment necessary to guarantee that the ibotenic acid was fully converted into muscimol. This means that there is a risk that the ibotenic acid levels in your dose may not be low enough to be considered safe if your dosage is larger than normal. Additionally, if you are new to microdosing, it is always recommended that you start your practice—especially with substances such as *Amanita muscaria* or psilocybin—in a safe and familiar environment, and it doesn't hurt to have someone else present or available by phone that you can trust in case you feel uncomfortable, or to even help you seek emergency medical attention should you start experiencing adverse effects due to taking a dose that is too high, or you have an unusual sensitivity to it that you didn't know about before.

How Does Decarboxylation Work?

When I talk about decarboxylation, I am referring to the chemical reaction where a carbon atom is separated from a line of connected carbon atoms (or carbon chain). Drinking carbonated beverages would reverse this process and turn muscimol back into ibotenic acid, and now that you know this fact, you might want to reconsider crossing carbonated drinks with Amanita muscaria either before, or after. It's not uncommon to experience nausea after ingesting Amanita muscaria, and one common "remedy" for nausea is to drink carbonated beverages which in this case would be inappropriate, you can use lemon instead.

An important point to take note of is that while it is best to collect freshly harvested *Amanita muscaria*, you **must not** eat them in their raw form. Fresh, raw fly agaric has high levels of ibotenic acid that can increase your risk of poisoning or result in severe adverse effects. When practicing techniques like microdosing, you have to ensure that you are taking the correct safety precautions for your overall well-being. Ignoring these steps will not make the mushroom work faster or better, you are only putting yourself at unnecessary risk.

In addition, the decarboxylation methods that I discuss throughout this book have been based on studies and reports but have not always been specifically studied. Decarboxylation's importance to the microdosing process may make this section one of the most important parts of the book. Please remember that this book has been written mainly for educational and informative purposes. You will be using this book and the information that it contains at your own discretion. I have compiled the following section based on my own research and experiences. Using this information, I was able to determine the optimal temperature and pH for decarboxylation methods at home.

Optimal Temperature

Some people think that decarboxylation always happens when the *Amanita muscaria* specimens are dried, tipically between 109 to 131°F (45 to 55°C) to be preserved—whether you are using an oven, dehydrator, or both—but no conversion will be taking place at these temperatures. What happens is that the amount of ibotenic acid is noticeably reduced, hardly affecting the muscimol content. And although potency is lost—having less ibotenic acid available to be converted to muscimol—it's still an important precautionary measurement against neurotoxins. In fact, the ibotenic acid concentration is reduced 4 times by drying at 176°F (80°C), hardly affecting the muscimol concentration (Tsonuda et al., 1993).

As for decarboxylating ibotenic acid to muscimol while drying, it will be more noticeable, roughly, above 165°F (72°C) and up to 30% of the ibotenic acid will be converted to muscimol.

However, the optimal temperature for a full decarboxylation of ibotenic acid to muscimol, in water, is just under 215°F (100°C), for at least 2-3 hours at a pH of 2,7 (Nielsen et al., 1985). This means that if we use fresh, raw *Amanita muscaria* that has been cut into pieces and placed in water at 215°F, we know that the full conversion of ibotenic acid will occur at approximately 3 hours—at a pH of 2,7—under perfectly controlled conditions. Some users follow this method (skipping the drying step), and the drained water is then stored in the fridge. The reason is simple to understand, fresh specimens contain the most ibotenic acid possible to convert during the decarboxylation process. I do find the drying step more practical for microdosing and for preserving my batch, though. I can simply get more mushrooms if my final mixed batch is not potent enough.

Optimal pH

You need to measure the pH of your mixture (pH measurements often refer to the liquid or tea form of *Amanita muscaria*). You can use a correctly calibrated pH meter to measure the liquid's pH. A mixture is considered to have an optimal pH when it measures a pH of 2.7. To achieve this, you would need the juice of at least one freshly squeezed lemon; however, as each lemon is different, it is best to measure your pH level until it reaches the correct acidity. You could also use citric acid to help you adjust your mixture's pH levels (Gruska, 2020).

While the temperatures and pH levels mentioned above have the potential ability to convert all of the ibotenic acid in your *Amanita muscaria* powder or mixture to muscimol, the results are not guaranteed unless you have the tools normally found in a laboratory. Additionally, it's believed among some individuals who use *Amanita muscaria* that storing the dried mushroom will lead to more decarboxylation; however, in Tsonuda's study—titled *Change in Ibotenic Acid and Muscimol Contents in Amanita muscaria during Drying, Storing or Cooking*—it was found that there are no significant changes in the concentration of both ibotenic acid and muscimol during the duration of storage (which was a 90-day period) (Tsonuda et al., 1993).

It's very important that you stay as updated as possible on the research conducted on *Amanita muscaria* as the results of studies, and reports from users, are always revealing new information, supporting what we currently know about fly agaric, or disproving beliefs—like the one mentioned above. Consider joining online communities or internet forums where you can share your microdosing experience with others. This also creates an opportunity to learn about new microdosing practices that you can use.

The Best Microdosing Practices

You may have already realized that a number of microdosing practices exist. These practices are often influenced by the substance you are using, its effects on your mind and body, as well as what you are using it for. Whatever your reason for using *Amanita muscaria*, it's important that you also take care of your mind and body while microdosing. The tips that I discuss in this section are mainly aimed at those who are new to the microdosing practice; however, as you start discovering what works for you, you can start adapting these practices to suit your needs and lifestyle. Essentially, while these practices are adaptable, they provide you with a good foundation for staying safe and taking care of yourself while microdosing.

Tips for Microdosing

According to my research, experience, and the microdosing experiences of others who use *Amanita muscaria* for improving their well-being, the following tips can help you get the most out of the experience.

Start With the Smallest Dosage Possible
While I have already discussed the possible dosages that you could use, a good way to start your microdosing experience is to start off with the lowest possible dosage.

This allows you to see how you are affected by fly agaric, if you have any adverse reactions, and its results. If you aren't affected by a very low dose, you can slowly increase it. When you start experiencing the effects that you are aiming for, then you know you have reached your optimal dosage, but if you start becoming adversely affected (I will discuss common and adverse side effects in Chapter 4 to help you make this determination), then you need to lower the dose. But you also have to remember that the results you are aiming for won't always happen after one dose, as it affects everyone differently and it needs time to be absorbed and used properly by your body.

Prepare for Nausea

Unfortunately, nausea is a common side effect of microdosing with *Amanita muscaria*. You need to prepare your body before taking your first dose by taking it either fifteen to thirty minutes before breakfast or eating light foods before the intake. If you do start experiencing nausea, you can lie down, eat ginger biscuits, or drink ginger tea to help ease the symptoms. If you do start vomiting, do your best to stay hydrated by taking small sips of water. Should your vomiting become intense or frequent, please seek immediate medical attention as severe vomiting can become dangerous. Nausea is another reason why I prefer taking a slightly higher dose in the evening—besides being able to sleep more deeply.

Use Journaling Techniques

Journaling is an extremely important practice when microdosing, as it helps you keep track during your practice, ensuring that you don't forget anything that might be important. It's a great way to record your microdosing experience, how each dose affects you, as well as how you have adjusted the dosage. This helps you keep track of your results and which dosages work, helping you improve your microdosing experience. I would also suggest noting what form you consumed the *Amanita muscaria* in so that you can identify which one had the most benefits and the least side effects.

How to Journal

Start by taking note of the date, time, form, and quantity of the substance's dosage. Then, as the dose starts to affect you, note the changes in your thoughts, behavior, and mood. You could also note whether there are any improvements in your creativity and energy levels, etc. Include how the intake affects your ailments and others, if any. And don't only write down the good things. Take note of any side effects, like nausea, and their severity. Write down any bad feelings or other changes that aren't desired too.

When you start your microdosing session, note how you feel at the beginning of the day, as well as at the end. You could even include a reflection at the end of the entry, perhaps written the day after you took your dose. This gives you time to process your experience and review your notes, allowing you to identify what changes you should make and what you will do the same during your next microdosing session.

Listen to Music

A positive state of mind is important when microdosing because substances like *Amanita muscaria* and psilocybin (which will be discussed in detail in Chapter 3) are often referred to as psychoactive substances due to their effect on the mind. A good headspace that allows you to stay calm will ensure better results. And if for any reason you do start experiencing a sense of altered reality, listening to your favorite playlist can probably help.

Meditate

This technique helps you cultivate a peaceful state of mind that can help you actively notice *what* is happening in your mind and body. This is important for understanding how *Amanita muscaria* affects you, especially as you adjust the dosage. Meditation is also useful for taking time to reflect on your microdosing experience and how you feel about it.

Have a Self-Care Day

It might be a good idea to have the day that you take your microdose as a day off. This is especially helpful in the beginning. This will give your body and mind time to adjust, allowing you to reflect on your experience, and help you determine whether the dosage you took impacted you in the way you desire. Taking proper care of yourself is important to ensuring your well-being and helping you maximize the positive impact of your experience.

Take Breaks

The human body has the ability to build up a tolerance to substances, including *Amanita muscaria*. When the tolerance is built up, a person might increase their dosage until they start experiencing the desired effects, but this can be dangerous—especially when using a substance like *Amanita muscaria* as it can have adverse effects when it's frequently taken in high doses. The break that you take will depend on how you are affected by fly agaric and how long it affects you after a course of doses. Breaks could be anywhere between two to five days or even a month.

Immerse yourself in nature

A personal tip, immerse yourself in nature whenever possible, I have always found this practice very fulfilling (with or without microdosing). This is commonly recommended when microdosing with Psilocybin mushrooms because it's said psilocybin has the ability to connect you with nature. But let me tell you that doing it while microdosing with Amanita muscaria feels as nice.

You can use the tips above to create the foundation for your microdosing practice in a way that ensures that you are taking proper care of your mind and body. Take time to adjust and alter these practices as you see fit, as what works for you won't always work for someone else.

Ways to Use *Amanita Muscaria and Recipes*

Amanita muscaria can be consumed in various forms. The form that it's ingested in can actually impact how it affects you. Many people who microdose with fly agaric prefer to use—from more to less relevant—dried *Amanita muscaria* caps (excluding the stem) in a capsule form, cured or fermented fly agaric that has been dried, using dried caps to make a tea, and in a tincture; however, decarboxylation of the ibotenic acid does not occur when used as a tincture—which is typically used externally in this form.

Forms of Amanita Muscaria Microdosing

We don't know the potency of each mushroom's fruit for certain because every single cap can have vastly different levels of ibotenic acid. To combat this, you can take your dried caps and turn them into a powder that is thoroughly mixed to ensure that it forms a homogenous mass, resulting in a relatively stable potency. Once your powder has been thoroughly mixed, you can find your optimal dose using the methods I have discussed throughout this chapter. In the section that follows, I have provided you with the possible forms that you could use *Amanita muscaria* in, depending on what you are aiming to achieve from its use.

Alcohol Tincture

Typically made using fresh *Amanita muscaria*, this alcohol tincture can be stored for many years in the fridge. Used externally, the tincture is useful when applied as a compress or a rub for individuals who experience musculoskeletal pain that includes nerve, muscle, ligament, and joint inflammation and itching; however, this list isn't exhaustive. As the tincture uses fresh fly agaric that has not undergone decarboxylation, it's not recommended that you use it internally, as you may experience the same negative effects as using fresh, raw *Amanita muscaria*. Despite this, some people take it in drops.

What's needed:

- 2–3 fresh *Amanita muscaria* mushrooms of medium size

- organic ethanol (I use Everclear)

- sterilized glass jar

- aluminion (to cover the final jar placed in the fridge)

Directions:

1. Properly clean and cut your mushrooms into 1 inch (2,5 cm) pieces and place them in a jar.

2. Pour ethanol to cover the mushrooms by approximately an inch. Put a plastic lid on the jar to seal it.

3. Let sit for 6-8 weeks in darkness at 39,2°F (4°C). Shake every few days to prevent mold from growing.

4. Once satisfied with your tincture, strain the contents of the jar, and discard any remaining material.

Tips:

The typical fresh caps and ethanol ratio I use is 16 oz (450 g) per 120 milliliters.

You can use fresh caps or dried fungus. I personally use recently harvested fresh caps for the highest potency. Since the quality of the tincture is closely tied to the quality of the alcohol, the best alcohol should be used (with a high concentration, ideally over 70%). The ethanol will strip all of the alcohol-soluble chemicals, compounds, and alkaloids out of the plant material.

Should you decide to use dried *Amanita muscaria*, to increase potency, you can let some alcohol evaporate by leaving the lid open for a controlled period. Alcohol is volatile, so you can use the technique I use if you are planning to use heat. Place a small pot full of *Amanita muscaria* alcohol inside a bigger pot full of water. Gradually turn up the heat until the inner pot begins to steam.

Additionally, you can use the final tincture as a base for other recipes like ointment or oil. You can store it in the fridge. Your tincture will remain user-friendly for years if stored correctly!

Ointment

An ointment containing fly agaric can be used for the same inflammatory processes mentioned previously, as well as for treating fungal diseases and skin damage. It can be kept stored in the fridge.

What's needed:

- olive oil, or any other cold-pressed oil like avocado oil

- coconut oil, beeswax, or vaseline

- milled, dried *Amanita muscaria* caps

Directions:

1. Combine the fat and mushroom cap powder in a 50/50 ratio, the oil is optional.

2. Before using, let it sit in the refrigerator for at least two to three weeks. The longer, the better.

3. Do not strain the solid particles from the ointment.

4. Mix the ointment thoroughly while placing the container in a pot with warm water.

Tea

Using a small amount of the powder and following a recipe, you can create an *Amanita muscaria* tea that further converts the remaining ibotenic acid to muscimol. When the tea is strained to remove the solids, you decrease the amount of nausea you may experience. If you are aiming to sleep better, drinking the tea before bed can help you as muscimol acts as a relaxant.

What's needed:

- 0.02 to 0.04 oz (0,5 to 1 g) *Amanita muscaria*

- 1 cup warm water

Directions:

1. The mushroom should be dried and broken up into small pieces. I use dried *Amanita muscaria* powder.

2. 150 to 194°F (65 to 90°C) is the optimum water temperature.

3. Heat to about 150 °F (65 °C) for around 20-30 minutes

4. Allow the tea some time to cool so that the powdered *Amanita muscaria* can sink to the bottom of the container before being discarded.

Tips:

You can place your dried A*manita muscaria powder in a* well-insulated thermos with hot water at the desired temperature (ideally just below boiling point) and leave it for a few hours for a better conversion to muscimol. You can keep it for 24 hours without worrying about any potency loss.

Amanita Muscaria Oil

Amanita muscaria oil hydrates, repairs, nourishes and smoothes wrinkles while enhancing the complexion. It can also serve as a base for the *Amanita muscaria* ointment.

What's needed:

- *Amanita muscaria* cap powder

- olive oil, or any good quality cold-pressed oil like avocado, jojoba, or grapeseed

Directions:

1. Infuse the oil for 5 weeks by mixing dried *Amanita muscaria* powder and the preferred oil at a 50-50 volume ratio.

2. Once infused, strain to remove coarse particles.

Cooked

The compounds found in fly agaric are water-soluble substances. As such, they can be removed through boiling, straining, and rinsing practices which will reduce—or even eliminate if done properly—the active compounds and toxins found in the caps of *Amanita muscaria*, and hence the negative and inebriating effects of this mushroom. This process allows you to eat it as if it were a gourmet mushroom; however, you have to ensure that you prepare it correctly.

What's needed:

- sliced Amanita muscaria mushrooms

- water

Directions:

1. Bring a saucepan to a boil after adding water.

2. Add mushroom slices and boil for 10-15 minutes.

3. Take the saucepan off the heat and remove the mushrooms with kitchen clamps, set aside.

4. Drain the mushroom water.

5. Put new water in your saucepan and bring it to a boil again.

6. Add the mushroom slices back in and boil for another 10-15 minutes. Better safe than sorry.

7. Take the saucepan off the heat and spoon out the mushrooms with kitchen clamps, discard the mushroom water.

How to Pickle Amanita Muscaria

Seasoning *Amanita muscaria* mushrooms with salt and fermenting them in brine is inspired by the traditional Japanese technique. You can pickle your mushrooms in vinegar if you're not confident with the fermenting process.

What's needed:

- *Amanita muscaria*

- filtered water

- splash of whey (you can actually use any juice extracted from another ferment)

- kitchen salt

Directions:

- Detoxifying

    - The mushrooms should be cut into bits and placed in a saucepan with 2 tablespoons of kitchen salt and roughly 6 quarts of water (5,67 liters) for every pound (453 g) of mushrooms.

    - Cover the saucepan, bring to a boil, and set a timer for 15 minutes.

- Salting

    - Remove the mushrooms after 15 minutes. They should be thoroughly rinsed, dried, and then placed in a glass jar.

    - Pour in enough water to cover the mushrooms by half an inch or 1,5 cm.

    - Weigh the water and mushrooms (not the container), then multiply that weight by 0.03 so you know how many grams of salt to add for the recommended 3% (this step is very important).

    - You can add a dash of whey or sauerkraut juice as a starter culture to speed things up.

- Fermentation

- Shake the jar, cover the top with cling film, put a lid on, and allow it to sit at room temperature for 5 to 10 days.

- Make sure the mushrooms are submerged in liquid at all times to avoid mold.

- Put them in the fridge for up to 5 days. If you prefer a stronger flavor, keep them out for an additional day or two.

- If kept constantly submerged and in the refrigerator, they'll last longer and continue to ferment slowly.

- Happy pickling!

Smoke It

There are individuals who smoke the dried *Amanita muscaria* mushroom, but I have never personally tried it.

Amanita muscaria can be used and ingested in many forms, but you have to ensure that you prepare it properly to make it safe to ingest, decreasing the chances of adverse effects. Additionally, you also need to be extremely careful about *where* you get your fly agaric from. If you buy them from an online supplier, you cannot always be certain about what *exactly* is in the capsule, especially if you don't know the supplier. You may even receive a different strain of the *Amanita* mushroom that could harm you, like the *Amanita pantherina*.

Key Takeaways

● There is no universal dosage when microdosing using *Amanita muscaria*; as such, no fixed statement can be made.

● Each cap has a different composition, and each individual is affected differently.

● The recommended optimal dosage may be too high or low for you, depending on your unique reaction to fly agaric.

● Decarboxylation is an extremely important process that can convert the neurotoxic ibotenic acid to muscimol.

● Various decarboxylation methods exist; however, drying the mushroom is a popular technique against poisoning with neurotoxins, and is often the first step to practicing microdosing.

- A number of microdosing practices exist. You can use them to create a practice suited to your needs.

- *Amanita muscaria* can be consumed in various forms, and the way that you ingest it may affect its impact on you.

Microdosing can be beneficial when safely practiced. But it also requires some experimentation when trying to determine the right dose of *Amanita muscaria*. You may be nervous about practicing microdosing, but don't let that hold you back from learning about it because there are a number of ways that microdosing can benefit your health, which I will discuss in Chapter 3 in more detail.

Chapter 3: Microdosing for Health Benefits

The potential health benefits of microdosing with *Amanita muscaria* outweigh the amount of work that you need to put in to use this mushroom safely. While I briefly discussed the potential health benefits of fly agaric in the previous chapters, I will expand on these benefits here and discuss some of the studies that have been conducted to support what we currently know. However, it's important that you remember that many of these studies are based on anecdotal evidence and reports of individuals who practice microdosing with *Amanita muscaria*.

After reading the previous two chapters, I think you can agree that this mushroom is often misunderstood. There is good reason for the caution that is displayed towards *Amanita muscaria*, but you must not allow that to stop you from at least learning about what it could potentially do for you. It may be safe to use when correctly prepared, but it still affects everyone differently. As such, I cannot guarantee the benefits that are discussed in this chapter. Even the research and studies conducted demonstrated that the results of microdosing often varied depending on a number of factors.

Many people may decide to pursue microdosing with *Amanita muscaria* in order to pursue its therapeutic potential, allowing for the promotion of relaxation and calm. This is also one of the reasons why fly agaric is used in holistic medicine in the present day. As this mushroom has started gaining interest and popularity, pharmaceutical organizations and holistic companies, like Psyched Wellness, are starting to conduct more detailed research on the medicinal properties of *Amanita muscaria*. So, what are the potential applications of its medicinal properties?

Potential Medical and Mental Health Applications

The medical and psychiatric application of *Amanita muscaria* is numerous; however, most of the current research often focuses on muscimol due to its beneficial effects. But you need to keep in mind that this mushroom contains a number of chemical compounds that could have the potential to improve your health. On its own, muscimol is an interesting molecule. Its influence on the GABA system is one of the main reasons why this compound is the one commonly studied when looking at the therapeutic potential of fly agaric.

When muscimol is singled out for study, it demonstrates the potential to alleviate and manage pain, depression, and anxiety. It has also been studied in terms of its impact on Parkinson's disease and epilepsy—which I discussed in Chapter 1. But just like any other substance, muscimol can affect you in more than one way. According to Ponieman (2022), muscimol can act as an anxiolytic (it has the ability to relieve anxiety), anti-inflammatory, muscle relaxant, analgesic (relieve or reduce the pain experienced without causing a loss of consciousness), antioxidant, and antispastic. However, this will also depend on the individual practicing microdosing and their reaction to this compound. Additionally, it has also been used to treat sore throats. From this information, it's easy to see that *Amanita muscaria* has a variety of applications, both internally and externally.

When researching the potential health benefits of *Amanita muscaria*, I have found that its analgesic properties allow it to be used as an effective form of pain relief. Individuals who struggle with arthritis, rheumatoid arthritis, musculoskeletal pain, menstrual pain, migraines, and neuropathic pain often take part in microdosing with fly agaric due to its analgesic abilities.

Additionally, it has been used to treat nail fungus, rheumatism inflammation, and even skin conditions. My passion for microdosing with *Amanita muscaria* partially stems from my own experience and the health benefits that I have obtained through microdosing.

When discussed in terms of mental health, microdosing with *Amanita muscaria* is often used for treating anxiety due to its anxiolytic effects, allowing for a decrease in anxiety and panic attacks (which are often more intense and with no apparent reason), as well as helping you manage severe anxiety. Its ability to improve your mood and boost your energy is helpful if you struggle with depression or even staying motivated. Your awareness of your mind and body, as well as your surroundings, is also improved because fly agaric has the ability to connect you with yourself. This form of microdosing can help improve your sleep habits and treat insomnia due to the analgesic properties of muscimol.

Additionally, *Amanita muscaria* has been used to help individuals overcome their addiction to a substance and make it through withdrawal, but I will discuss this topic more in the section that follows.

However, the lack of studies regarding the health benefits of fly agaric in the modern, clinical setting means that a lot of the information that is used to promote microdosing, and that I have used to compile this book, is based on anecdotal evidence and reports.

Although anecdotal evidence is just as important as empirical evidence because it provides us with information based on experience. Sometimes experience is the best way to learn about whether or not something has the potential to be effective. In the following section, I have expanded more on the benefits discussed here by using the anecdotal evidence currently available.

Studies Supporting the Impact on Your Mental and Physical Health

The application of microdosing with fly agaric in terms of mental health and the medical field has not been widely studied; as such, I will look at Dr. Masha's study along with a few additional studies that were conducted on the specific components and chemicals found in *Amanita muscaria*.

While the research regarding these applications is based mainly on anecdotal evidence, we count on thousands of reports. Unfortunately, the downside of these reports is they weren't controlled. But that doesn't mean that the data that was gathered is irrelevant; if anything, it provides practical evidence that supports *Amanita muscaria's* potential application in the medical and mental health fields. This is a great starting point to get people's and scientists' attention, and she has all my respect.

When studying the project in depth, I found that her reports supported the information and research that I previously found while studying the potential of *Amanita muscaria* microdosing for alleviating the pain caused by my polyarthritis. The project obtained a large amount of data that I will briefly discuss that supports the information that I mentioned above. I will also discuss some additional studies that support the potential benefits of fly agaric in improving your mental and physical health.

An Overview of an Anecdotal Study

Dr. Masha was able to obtain the data needed for her study by studying anecdotal evidence that took the form of feedback reports provided by the project's participants. I have briefly discussed the most relevant feedback in the section that follows.

Analgesic or Painkiller

Musculoskeletal pain, which includes tendons, muscles, joints, ligaments, and bones, can negatively impact your quality of life if not treated, particularly if it's chronic. This pain can be debilitating and can include autoimmune diseases. Autoimmune diseases are conditions where your immune system's cells mistakenly attack your body's healthy tissues (NIAMS, 2017). Of the 477 participants, 70% (333) reported positive effects on their arthritis, including rheumatoid arthritis.

Rheumatoid arthritis

This form of arthritis is closely related to polyarthritis and ankylosing spondylitis. From the study, 91% (21) of 23 participants reported improvements after microdosing with *Amanita muscaria* or using it as a tincture that could be applied to the area experiencing pain and inflammation.

These results are supported by a study conducted by Ruthes et al. (2013). Fucomannogalactan and glucan—found in *Amanita muscaria*—have the potential to inhibit inflammatory pain, while ethanolic extract may be able to act as an anti-inflammatory (Ruthes et al., 2013; Biziulevičius & Vaitkuvienė, 2007).

Neuropathic Pain

A person may develop this chronic pain condition when they experience an event or injury that triggers the delivery of pain signals to their brain, regardless of whether the body was actually experiencing physical pain or not. This condition is often caused by injury, progressive nerve disease, and infection. Of the 64 participants, 86% experienced positive effects after microdosing.

Migraines

A common neurological disease (a condition affecting your brain or nerves) that causes severe throbbing pain, or a pulsating sensation, on one side of the head. Thirty-five million people in the US suffer from migraine headaches, and it affects more women than men (The Migraine Institute, 2016).

There are a number of reasons why a person may experience migraines, including a family history of this condition, sleep issues, depression, anxiety, etc. It may not seem as though this disease can be debilitating from an outsider's perspective, but the pain it causes—along with additional symptoms—can make it feel like torture for the person suffering from the migraine.

Additional symptoms such as vomiting, nausea, visual disturbances, difficulty speaking, tingling in the arms and legs, as well as extreme sensitivity to light and sound often accompany a migraine (Mayo Clinic, 2021c). The data showed that 65% (72) of 110 participants suffering from migraines experienced positive effects.

Sleeping Aid

Sleep issues can be caused by mental disorders, health conditions, side effects from taking drugs and some medications, stress, as well as a number of other health-related conditions. Of the 980 participants in the survey who used *Amanita muscaria* microdosing as a sleep aid, 73% experienced positive effects, although 10% experienced insomnia as a negative side effect.

Cold

You may already be familiar with the common cold. This viral infection affects your upper respiratory tract and results in common symptoms such as a sore throat, runny nose, cough, and congestion. When microdosing with *Amanita muscaria*, 78% (145) of 186 participants experienced positive improvements in their recovery from colds.

Allergies

Many people suffer from seasonal allergies, and while the allergy itself might not be cured, *Amanita muscaria* microdosing may have the potential to manage its symptoms. The study's data revealed that 59% (61) of 104 of the participants who suffered from allergies experienced positive effects and a decrease in their symptoms.

Constipation

Some people struggle with the irregular release of their bowels, resulting in conditions such as constipation. While diet is often targeted in managing this condition, microdosing has also shown the potential in helping these individuals go more regularly. Out of 192 participants who normally struggled with constipation, 58% reported that they had become more regular, struggling less with constipation-related issues.

Nail Fungus

Microdosing with *Amanita muscaria* was used to treat nail fungus in 245 participants, with 53% experiencing improvements in their condition. This is supported by a study that was conducted on Hydroxypyrrolidine—a compound found in *Amanita muscaria*—in relation to its known antibacterial and antifungal properties (Matsumoto et al., 1969).

Hypertension

This systemic condition occurs when an individual's blood pressure is abnormally high. Microdosing was reported to improve hypertension in 73% out of 63 participants.

Psoriasis

While not contagious, this chronic disease can be painful, making it difficult for a person to concentrate, and interferes with their sleep. This autoimmune disease takes the form of a scaly rash that can be extremely itchy and is normally found on the scalp, elbows, trunk, and knees of a person's body. Out of 54 participants, 65% experienced positive effects.

Swelling of the Lower Extremities

Swelling often occurs as a result of inflammation, fluid retention, and injury. As a result, your joints, skin, tissues, and organs may increase in size. When this type of swelling occurs in your lower extremities, it's normally expressed in your legs. You may experience fatigue and cramps in your legs, as well as a number of additional symptoms that can cause you pain and discomfort. Microdosing with *Amanita muscaria*, and using it in the form of a tincture, had an overall positive effect on 83% (39) of 47 participants.

Other Conditions Studied Include:

Goiter

Individuals who struggle with managing and treating their goiter also took part. Goiter is a condition where a person's thyroid gland becomes so enlarged from swelling, for a number of reasons, that it is visible from the front of the neck. After microdosing with *Amanita muscaria* for the duration of the study, it was found that 88% (15) of 17 participants experienced positive effects on their goiter.

Additionally, microdosing showed improvements in around half of the participants in regard to heartburn, eczema, menstrual pain, and libido. And participants with autism and epilepsy provided feedback on their microdosing experience and 77% reported improvements, both separately.

Effects on Mental Health

When looking at the impact of *Amanita muscaria* on mental health, 999 participants struggling with asthenia (a loss of strength, lack of energy, and increased occurrences of fatigue), depression, and existential agony said they had experienced a 79% improvement. Microdosing with *Amanita muscaria* was also reported to be effective in reducing anxiety and panic attacks.

Muscimol was studied in terms of its potential ability to reduce the conditioned fear response, something that is important in treating and managing anxiety disorders. Wilensky et al. (2006) found that muscimol's anxiolytic properties may be able to help manage and reduce anxiety (Wilensky et al., 2006).

Influence on Addiction and Withdrawal

When Dr. Masha studied the effect of *Amanita muscaria* on addiction, it was found that half of the 400 participants experienced stable and prolonged results and reduced their alcohol consumption. Out of these participants, 35% of them stopped drinking.

The consumption of marijuana was also studied in 169 participants and showed 57% of the participants experienced positive results, with 13% of them quitting, as well as positive results in half of the nicotine dependence (49% of 196 participants).

Just under 100 of the participants were using other types of drugs. Between 68% to 88% of them reported positive effects after microdosing, while 12% to 26% quit completely.

Microdosing with *Amanita muscaria* has a number of benefits for your mental and physical health, but you also need to take into consideration your unique reaction to the mushroom. The anecdotal evidence provides promising information, but its benefits cannot be guaranteed.

Improving Your Well-Being

While *Amanita muscaria* can be used to improve your overall health, especially if you have medical or mental health conditions, it can also be used to positively impact your general well-being. Everyday life has become stressful, and it's easier than ever to get burnt out physically, mentally, and emotionally. It's easy for others to say that you simply need to take time for yourself to relax, but what works for them won't always work for you. If you need a bit of extra help, that's nothing to be ashamed of. Microdosing with *Amanita muscaria* can help you improve your overall well-being, regardless of why you want to try it. But you need to remember that your reaction to fly agaric will be unique and you cannot guarantee how you will be affected.

Some of the many positive impacts that this type of microdosing can provide include increasing your energy levels, helping you feel motivated, boosting your productivity, improving your mood, ability to concentrate and focus, relational skills, as well as being able to increase your creativity levels. Simply put, *Amanita muscaria* is beneficial to your well-being due to muscimol's ability to calm your brain down and hinder glutamate and stress' stimulating impact on the mind (Ponieman, 2022).

One thing I do want to focus on is the ability of *Amanita muscaria* to improve your sleep. I briefly mentioned it in the previous section, but it's applicable here too because sleep has such an important impact on the mind and body, and ultimately, your well-being. When you don't get enough sleep, your immune system may be lowered, you might struggle to react appropriately to a situation, or you could experience an increase in lethargy.

Dr. Masha also studied the reports of how participants' overall well-being had been impacted by microdosing with *Amanita muscaria*. Her findings were also supported by some additional studies that were based on anecdotal evidence and in vivo findings.

Studies Supporting the Impact of Microdosing on Your Well-Being

During Dr. Masha's study, she also researched the potential of *Amanita muscaria* to improve a person's well-being, sleeping habits, and treatment of insomnia. I have briefly discussed these results in the section that follows.

Improved Creativity

While it can be normal to struggle with feeling creative sometimes, microdosing may be able to help you improve your creativity levels. Of the 262 participants, 63% experienced an increase in their creativity.

Increased Energy Levels, Mood, and Vitality

While struggling with your energy levels may be indicative of an underlying condition, you may want to improve your energy levels to better keep up with the demands of daily life. Individuals may also struggle with managing their mood, or even feeling creative, regardless of whether they struggle with their mental health or not. Increased energy levels and improvements in mood and vitality, and fewer—or less severe—panic attacks were reported by 88% of the almost 1,000 participants.

Improved Sleep

Struggling to sleep, or finding it difficult to sleep well, can be caused by a variety of health conditions, but you might also struggle with sleep because of stressful life events, trauma, anxiety, jet lag, or simply because you are overwhelmed by the demanding, everyday rat race. It was found in the study that 73% of the participants experienced improved sleep, sometimes experiencing vivid dreams. This supports the theory that *Amanita muscaria* could have the ability to restore your sleeping patterns; although, empirical studies have yet to be completed on this topic.

Gaboxadol is a compound that is also found in *Amanita muscaria* that has analgesic and sleep-promoting properties. This substance may also have the potential to restore sleep patterns and treat insomnia (Krogsgaard-Larsen, 2018; Johnston et al., 2022). And by now you should know that muscimol has been shown to promote a relaxing state and restorative sleep.

Increased Performance and Stamina

If you take part in sports—professionally or as a hobby—microdosing with *Amanita muscaria* may have the potential to improve your performance and increase your stamina. Dr. Masha studied the feedback from fighters—who had agreed to take part in her study—on their performance. The fighters reported a positive improvement in their performance and stamina.

Improved Immune System Functioning

Psyched Wellness is a company that produces health products based on the research they conducted on *Amanita muscaria*'s medicinal properties. They conducted a study in vivo, on a compound called "AME-1" that was created from the fly agaric mushroom. Their study found that this compound could potentially improve your immune system's ability to function, increase its response to pathogens, maintain this efficiency, and promote overall gut health (Price, 2022).

Amanita muscaria is a versatile mushroom with many health benefits and the potential to improve your well-being. As microdosing with this mushroom becomes more popular, it's important that you stay updated with new studies and research—even if it's based on anecdotal evidence—as it may provide you with the opportunity to improve your own microdosing practices. But fly agaric isn't the only mushroom used for microdosing.

Comparison to Microdosing Psilocybin

You may be more familiar with the psilocybin mushroom than you are with *Amanita muscaria*. This psychedelic mushroom, commonly known as a "magic mushroom," has also been used by individuals to practice microdosing. However, the benefits that they seek can sometimes be similar to those received from fly agaric, so what's the difference?

Paul Stamets described psilocybin mushrooms as nature's messengers. Simply put, psilocybin connects you with nature, while *Amanita muscaria* connects you with your inner self. Both of these mushrooms can affect your mind. Psilocybin is known for its powerful, psychedelic properties due to its interactions with a specific serotonin receptor in your brain. Additionally, it doesn't improve your sleep directly like Amanita muscaria can do, nor treat as many somatic diseases—or even combat them—lacking the potential to treat skin pathologies like warts, eczema, psoriasis, and skin pigmentation. You may have heard psilocybin isn't able to manage or decrease pain due to a lack of analgesic properties; still, you must know it has shown anti-inflammatory properties and has been used to alleviate pain including discomfort caused by cancer, phantom limb pain, migraine, and—with unbelievable effectiveness—cluster headaches (also known as "suicide headaches," because of evident reasons).

Psilocybin is a powerful substance that has the ability to improve your performance, creativity, concentration, and cognitive functioning, increase your energy levels and physical stamina, improve your verbal fluency and relational skills, help you stay productive, increase your mood, improve your concentration, enhance your senses, and alleviate symptoms of anxiety and depression. As such, its benefits focus mainly on your mental well-being. Psilocybin can improve a person's psychological functioning by decreasing anxiety levels, reducing the number—or severity–of panic attacks, combating negative emotions, and decreasing aggression. Additionally, psilocybin can help break addictive habits. New studies are being done as you read this to see if magic mushrooms can be used to treat PTSD, OCD, and several mental health conditions. If you would like to find out more about microdosing psilocybin, I invite you to check out my book *"Microdosing Psilocybin Mushrooms: An Essential*

Guide to Microdosing Magic Mushrooms & Microdosing Journal."

In comparison, *Amanita muscaria* cannot necessarily be classified as a psychedelic mushroom because muscimol can interact with the GABAa receptors without inducing the same psychedelic effects of mushrooms like psilocybin. Additionally, it doesn't work like other psychedelic mushrooms. Muscimol suppresses the activity of neurons in your brain, while ibotenic acid—which can trigger the glutamate receptors—interrupts their communication. In comparison, psilocybin's active compounds interact with your brain's serotonin and dopamine transmitters.

Both *Amanita muscaria* and psilocybin can be effectively used for microdosing practices, but the one that you choose will depend on the benefits that you are looking for. If you struggle with deciding, I invite you to learn more about psilocybin from my other books about psilocybin mushrooms. You can also read the studies conducted on both of these mushrooms, or even join online community forums where you can learn about the experiences that others had when microdosing with these mushrooms. The choice is ultimately yours but allow yourself to take the time to do the research so that your decision is informed, and you know the possible risks and benefits you could achieve with the mushroom you choose.

Key Takeaways

- The versatility of *Amanita muscaria* allows it to have a number of medicinal applications.

- It can be used to treat internal and external health conditions.

- Both your mental and physical health can benefit from microdosing with *Amanita muscaria.*

- You need to remember that your unique reaction to fly agaric will impact the benefits you experience.

- Regardless of whether you have an existing or underlying health condition, you can use this mushroom to help you improve your overall well-being.

- *Amanita muscaria* doesn't work exactly like other psychedelic mushrooms, and it often has more benefits in terms of improving your physical health.

While microdosing with *Amanita muscaria* can benefit your health in a number of ways, you also need to have a good understanding of the possible adverse, or common, side effects you could face and how to deal with them. Remember that safety will be your top priority throughout the microdosing practice.

Chapter 4: Possible Adverse or Common Side Effects

You wouldn't go hiking in the Himalayan mountains without any preparation. Well, this is a journey. These are sacraments and medicines that should be treated with respect and caution. –Paul Stamets

Just as you would with any other medication, it's important that you treat *Amanita muscaria* with the same respect. Incorrect preparation and high doses can negatively impact you, resulting in adverse side effects. Additionally, just as any other medication has side effects—even when correctly used—so can fly agaric. The information contained in this book provides you with information that could help you safely and respectfully use *Amanita muscaria* for microdosing, but you also need to be aware of the common side effects, as well as the possible adverse effects, should you handle it incorrectly. Mistakes happen. It's part of being human, which is why it's important that you know what these possible adverse and common side effects are, how to minimize your risk, and what to do should you experience these effects.

Side Effects Most Commonly Experienced

Each *Amanita muscaria* mushroom has varying levels of potency, which is why no fixed statements can be made regarding dosage. As such, you may experience some side effects while you work to identify the correct dosage. But there are also a number of common side effects that could affect you—due to your unique reaction—even when taking the correct dosage. The first step to combating the possible common side effects that you could experience is to know what they are. The following list includes some of the more common side effects that have been reported by those who have used fly agaric for microdosing:

- nausea

- dizziness

- an uncomfortable feeling in your stomach, sometimes resulting in vomiting

- lack of focus

- diarrhea

- headache

- vivid dreaming

- hallucinations

- increased sweating

- lack of energy, possibly resulting in sedation

- loss of coordination

- salivation

- altered perception of your body

Impact of Dosage on Common Side Effects

While your experience will differ, individuals who practice microdosing have reported a number of common symptoms at different dosage levels. You will notice that some of these symptoms have already been mentioned in both the list above and throughout the previous chapters, except their severity can be impacted by the dosage.

Microdoses

A lower dose of *Amanita muscaria* can result in side effects such as possible gastrointestinal discomfort, nausea, loss of coordination, lethargy, pain in the kidney area, fatigue, vivid dreams, heartburn, and other effects that are similar to those of ingesting alcohol. It may also have a relaxing effect, help relieve pain, or even cause you to perspire more than normal.

Higher Doses

Higher doses often have a more intense impact on your mind and body. Effects include nausea and vomiting, dizziness; a distinct change in how you perceive yourself and your surroundings, possibly resulting in hallucinations (visual, auditory, and tactile); lucid dreaming, dysphoric mood, repetitive behaviors, severe gastrointestinal distress, and possibly diarrhea, a decrease in your blood pressure, confusion, amnesia, and the possible loss of control over your muscles.

Side effects experienced at higher dosage levels can result in adverse side effects that could become dangerous. Fortunately, there aren't many known deaths that were caused by *Amanita muscaria* poisoning. As such, seeking medical attention can help you recover from adverse side effects.

Personally, I never used *Amanita muscaria* to trip and I never will; as such, I would not recommend it as it isn't worth the risk. On the other hand, I did trip with psilocybin many times—as it's the safest drug, if used responsibly (Global Drug Survey 2017).

Adverse Side Effects

Your microdosing experience will be unique to you. These effects can also be dose-dependent. High doses of *Amanita muscaria*, along with incorrect preparation, can result in adverse effects.

- Depending on your family's genetic history, you may be predisposed to drug-induced psychosis.

- Trauma may occur if you aren't in a safe environment, especially when taking a high dosage that was incorrectly prepared.

- You must remember that ibotenic acid becomes neurotoxic if your body isn't able to metabolize it through the enzymes of your digestive tract, resulting in the activation of the passage of calcium ions to neurons, causing the neuron's death.

- If you don't correctly identify the *Amanita muscaria* mushroom, you could end up using a more toxic *Amanita* species—like *Amanita pantherina*—resulting in mushroom poisoning.

- In severe cases or reactions, a person may experience seizures, periods of central nervous system depression, loss of consciousness, or even a comatose state. Such severe cases are rare and often result from ingesting the fresh, raw mushroom and incorrect preparation.

If you find yourself in trouble, the best thing you can do is to seek emergency medical attention, which is why I recommend another sober individual be present while you practice microdosing. Healthcare providers will provide you with supportive treatment that is based on your symptoms and how you are being affected by the mushroom.

Some examples of possible treatments—which I don't encourage being practiced at home—include administering activated charcoal to limit the absorption of most toxins, and it helps your body get rid of the mushrooms from your gastrointestinal tract. Adverse symptoms, like seizures, may result in the administration of the appropriate anticonvulsants. The effects of a strong dose normally last up to 24 hours, but you can recover completely with supportive treatment; however, recurrent consumption of high doses— especially of fresh, raw fly agaric—can become dangerous to your continued health (Buschfunkistan, 2019). It is not worth the risk.

Pantherina Poisoning Syndrome

Amanita pantherina is among one of the many mushrooms normally responsible for trips to the emergency room as a result of misidentification. As such, poisoning by this mushroom has been named "pantherina poisoning syndrome." According to Çağdaş Yıldırım et al. (2016), this syndrome is characterized by the dysfunction of your central nervous system.

Additionally, symptoms of this syndrome include coma, deep sleep, vivid color perception, ataxia, fatigue, confusion, muscle spasms, nausea, hallucinations, dizziness, and delirium. Your unique reaction and medical history will also play an important role in diagnosing and treating mushroom poisoning, regardless of the genus. However, healthcare providers will start with supportive treatment, based on your reaction.

Amanita pantherina (*Amanitaceae*) and *Amanita muscaria* are both among the many mushroom species suspected of having a similar negative effect on a person's mind and body. The individuals that are commonly admitted with this type of poisoning include young children, those looking to experience a hallucinatory high, wild mushroom foragers, and even individuals aiming to attempt suicide or homicide.

I would not recommend using *Amanita muscaria* to trip as—from what I have seen and found through research— it simply isn't worth the risk. As such, I don't approve of—and never will approve of—the use of this mushroom to achieve a hallucinatory state; this especially includes the use of *Amanita pantherina* (also known as "Panther cap") for experimentation. The majority of the bad news related to *Amanita muscaria* that I have seen is often due to irresponsible use and the ingestion of *Amanita pantherina*. If you are practicing microdosing, it is important that you always practice caution and take the necessary steps to remain safe throughout the process.

Interactions With Other Drugs

Unfortunately, due to a lack of research on *Amanita muscaria*, we don't fully understand how it will interact with other substances, such as medications, alcohol, and drugs. I recommend that you speak with your personal healthcare provider if you are thinking about using

Amanita muscaria to practice microdosing, especially if you are already taking medications and supplements.

What Does the Data Say?

When looking at Baba Masha's research project, negative effects were reported by 7% of the 552 participants. The occurrence of pre-existing conditions and their severity were not taken into account here. Fortunately, many of the individuals who had negative symptoms experienced light side effects that went away shortly after the microdosing course was continued.

Additionally, a clear correlation was found between nausea and the weight of the participant's *Amanita muscaria* microdose. Nausea was observed in only 1 in every 10 participants who took a dosage of up to 0.04 oz (1 g), as well as in 70% of the participants who took 0.11 oz (3 g) and above. Changes in perception were also observed in 0.11 oz (3 g). These changes were also found to increase proportionally to the weight of the participant's dosage.

Safety Precaution Tips

- Ensure that you are using an *Amanita muscaria* mushroom and not another, more toxic, species.

- Fresh, raw *Amanita muscaria* has a high ibotenic acid to muscimol ratio. As such, when you ingest it raw, this level can quickly build up in your system and put you at risk of developing adverse side effects.

- Ensure that you are correctly preparing your fly agaric before using it. This includes starting out with very small doses due to variations in potency between each mushroom.

Who's Disqualified From the Clinical Trials

I have previously mentioned that your reaction to *Amanita muscaria* will be unique. As such, you may be wondering: "How do I know if I should avoid microdosing with *Amanita muscaria*?" You have to remember that there isn't a lot of research available; however, anecdotal reports revealed that there were a few different individuals that should avoid microdosing with fly agaric or taking part in trials that use this mushroom. Kindly note that these lists aren't exhaustive due to a lack of research and studies on this mushroom.

Due to the lack of research on how fly agaric can affect you, pregnant or breastfeeding mothers should avoid microdosing with this mushroom as we cannot be certain how this will affect the fetus or impact the pregnancy. Please, be careful.

If your family has a history of chronic mental health disorders, or you are predisposed to such mental conditions, then you need to be cautious about microdosing with *Amanita muscaria* as it can aggravate or trigger dormant psychotic disorders or increase your risk of adverse effects. Such disorders include schizophrenia, bipolar disorder, etc.

Additionally, individuals who struggle with kidney stones may want to avoid microdosing with *Amanita muscaria*, according to Baba Masha (2022:115-127), it's possible for fly agaric to trigger the removal of these stones from your bladder and kidneys.

If you are still unsure about whether you should avoid microdosing with *Amanita muscaria*, but you are interested in this practice, you can always consult with your healthcare provider. They will be able to help you determine if you have any conditions (mental or physical) that could be triggered or adversely affected by microdosing. They may even be able to provide you with more guidance on how to practice microdosing safely if there is a concern due to family history or prior medical conditions. Don't be afraid to take the necessary precautions that could help you ensure your safety and health.

Key Takeaways

- Microdosing with *Amanita muscaria* has side effects, just like any other medication.

- There are a number of common side effects, but their severity often depends on your dosage and sensitivity to the substances.

- Adverse side effects normally result from incorrect preparation and taking high doses.

- Higher doses of *Amanita muscaria* are not safe.

- Mushroom poisoning and adverse effects also result from incorrect identification of the fly agaric mushroom.

- *Amanita pantherina* is a more toxic mushroom that gets mistaken for *Amanita muscaria*, resulting in "Pantherina poisoning syndrome."

- You should never combine fly agaric with other substances (legal or illegal), like drugs, medication, and alcohol, as we don't fully understand their possible interactions.

- Before practicing microdosing, ensure that your family doesn't have a history of physical or mental illness that could result in adverse side effects, possibly even triggering the early onset of these conditions.

Knowing what the possible risks of microdosing with *Amanita muscaria* are, being able to identify common side effects, and what steps you can take to ensure your continued safety are important in helping you understand exactly what the risks are when pursuing microdosing practices. Chapter 5 will teach you how to hunt, dry, and preserve your *Amanita muscaria* safely.

Chapter 5: Hunting, Drying, and Preserving Your *Amanita Muscaria*

While you can order *Amanita muscaria* online, there is no better feeling than going to forage for your own medicine, I personally love it. However, you do need to be careful when gathering wild mushrooms because there are a number of toxic species that exist. Fortunately, it isn't easy to mistake *Amanita muscaria* as it doesn't have many close lookalikes. But you do need to know *where* to find fly agaric and *how* to correctly identify this mushroom. And I will walk you by the hand and teach you how to differentiate the good from the bad.

Mushroom Hunting and Identification

Mushrooms come in all shapes and sizes. Even when they are from the same species their size and shape can be vastly different, which is why a person may end up picking a more dangerous species of mushroom. As such, you have to closely examine your mushrooms before picking them. Take pictures that you can share with other experienced mushroom foragers, online forums, or Facebook groups that can help you ensure that you identified the correct mushroom. Consider taking a course on mushroom foraging and identification or contact your local mushroom experts (who can be found through an internet search) and ask them if they'd be willing to teach you how to forage for mushrooms safely. Remember, safety is key!

Kindly note: *Amanita muscaria* is not native to many of the areas where it can be found in. In order to protect local ecosystems and other native species, you need to take the necessary precautions when foraging for this mushroom. During the gathering process, it's easy to spread its spores accidentally, as they can attach themselves to your clothing without you knowing, be transported by water after rainfall, as well as being spread by air currents. In fact, did you know that we breathe fungal spores every time we inhale? It's important that those of us who gather these mushrooms take our local environment into consideration by staying informed and doing what we can to avoid the spread of these spores in areas where they are not naturally found. It's recommended that mushroom foragers clean their shoes and wear clean clothes when entering and foraging in such areas. Although it is a good practice to drop the spores of the specimens we find for future harvest, as you can see this doesn't apply to every habitat in which you find Amanita muscaria.

Additionally, every country and local area (especially nature reserves) will have specific laws regarding the gathering of wild mushrooms in general. Ensure that you familiarize yourself with such rules and regulations.

When hunting for *Amanita muscaria* in your local environment, you should keep two key points in mind:

- Do not collect mushrooms that are old, damaged, or look like they have been eaten by animals or worms.

- For *Amanita muscaria* microdosing, we collect only the caps of mushrooms. The cap contains the main concentration of active substances, specifically in the skin of the cap and in the yellow-white layer underneath it.

When hunting *Amanita muscaria*, you can use the information in the section below to help you correctly identify the mushroom.

Identifying Amanita Muscaria

Also known as "Fly Agaric," this mushroom is believed to have been collected by the shamans of Central Asia. Dressed in black boots, red pants, and coats trimmed with white fur, shamans would collect *Amanita muscaria* mushrooms and deliver them to the people of their village. Tales detailing their actions are believed to have inspired the modern *Santa Claus* story, especially as the doors of villagers were often snowed shut, causing shamans to enter yurts through their smoke holes.

Villagers would then place their mushrooms in socks and hang them above the fire to dry.

Habitat

Amanita muscaria mushrooms always grow directly from the ground, in both low-altitude areas, and in high mountains, in widespread habitats of the temperate and boreal zones of the Northern Hemisphere. This mushroom is often found in groups where you can typically notice specimens in different stages of development. They are normally found in acidic, sandy soils, among the roots of cedar, oak, birch, pine, and fir trees as a result of their symbiotic relationship (*mycorrhizae*), so pay attention to what trees are growing around these specimens. Fly agaric is native to deciduous and conifer forests.

Hunting Months

In northern countries and North America, it can be found in the late summer and autumn months. On the Pacific Coast, fruiting typically occurs later in autumn and early winter. In most parts of Europe, you can start finding them in May through to autumn. Mushroom fruiting will be dependent on prior soil moisture and rain.

Please take note that the levels of ibotenic acid and muscimol will vary at different times of the year. Normally, you can find up to 10 times more ibotenic acid and muscimol in the spring and summer flushes of fly agaric, compared to the autumn ones.

Caps

When *Amanita muscaria* first emerges from the ground, it looks like an egg. The mushrooms are covered in a whitish membrane—known as the "universal membrane"—that breaks as they begin to grow, creating the pointy white warts, which are normally visible if not removed by the rain. The cap starts turning red as the veil breaks, and the warts become less prominent. Although, the warts don't actually change size; instead, they look smaller because the cap gets larger and changes from a round shape to a hemispherical one before becoming the flat, plate-like cap that we are familiar with, sometimes becoming slightly concave or upturned. Keep in mind that the white fragments on the cap can wash off with heavy rain. Just like everything else, fly agaric also goes through various life stages. *Amanita muscaria* variation *guessowii*, also known as "American yellow fly agaric," typically grows in North

America and has a reddish-yellow or reddish-orange cap.

When they are mature, the cap will measure between 3 to 8 inches (8 to 20 cm) in diameter; although, it is possible for it to be larger. The mushroom caps, as they get older and are exposed to nature's elements, the red color fades into orange before turning yellow. Heavy rain can speed up this process. There is also a yellowish layer of skin underneath the cap that can be seen when it's cut open.

Additionally, the red color from the surface slightly extends down into the cap flesh, just a few millimeters. You will see this better if you cut the mushroom in half. The flesh inside the cap is white, and if the specimen is fresh, it will have a firm texture.

Gills

Amanita muscaria has tight or crowded, but free gills. They are white but turn pale yellow when the mushroom ages. The gills are free from the stem and grow inwards.

Stem or Stipe

The stem is white, normally with a hanging white ring (but not always there), also known as the "annulus" or "skirt" felted—almost scaly—in texture and cylindrical in shape, easily separated from the cap, and it has a bulbous base, typically like an egg just underground. At the mature stage, it can grow to about 2.0 to 7.9 inches (5 to 20 cm) in length, and 0.5 to 1 inch (1,0 to 2.5 cm) wide. An important characteristic is the multiple rings of tissue that can be found at the top of the volva, but again, not always. Check the rest of the specimens of the group, if none have it, then you might want to consider they are different species. Something you might want to know additionally, is that the volva covers the entire mushroom when it starts growing, the white warts on the cap are the leftovers.

Spores

Spores are ellipsoidal in shape and measure between 9 to 13 micrometers (μm) by 6.5 to 9 μm. They are smooth, hyaline, and non-amyloid. However, you would need a microscope to be able to identify spore characteristics. Additionally, spores do not turn blue if iodine in the form of Melzer's Reagent is applied (non-amyloid).

Spore Print

The color of the spore print of fly agaric is pure white.

Deadly, to avoid, and other lookalikes

Deadly and to Avoid

Amanita muscaria isn't easily mistaken for other, more dangerous mushroom species, but mistakes do happen. I will provide you with some of the mushrooms that are close to, or can resemble, fly agaric and how to identify them. There are a variety of *Amanita species,* and due to the various life stages that all mushrooms go through, it is possible to mistake a more dangerous species of mushroom for *Amanita muscaria* at certain stages. In the section that follows, I have provided you with a brief overview of some of these species, including dangerous ones, as well as why they may be mistaken for fly agaric.

Amanita Phalloides

Commonly known as the "Death Cap," this mushroom is not only toxic but deadly as well. The danger is that it resembles a number of edible mushrooms. The cap starts out hemispherical before expanding and flattening as it matures. Normally a yellowish-green color, the cap of this mushroom has also been recorded as having a pale green, bronze, and olive-green color. While the cap's surface is normally dry and shiny, it becomes sticky when wet.

Amanita Pantherina

Also known as *Amanita phanterina*, "panther cap," and "false blusher." It contains high levels of ibotenic acid and muscimol, meaning its depressant qualities are stronger than fly agaric's. Additionally, the cap of this mushroom is brown. Avoid this one.

Amanita Frostiana

Commonly found in the eastern US and southeastern Canada, this poisonous mushroom has a flat, shield-shaped cap. Normally, the cap is red, reddish-pink, or yellow in color with distinctive striations, or lines, around the margin. These lines are used to differentiate this mushroom from *Amanita muscaria*. Additionally, this mushroom is also smaller than fly agaric.

Other Lookalikes

Amanita Caesarea

Not poisonous, but a highly coveted mushroom in gastronomy. Often mistaken for *Amanita muscaria* without its warts—which may have been lost due to heavy rain—and whose cap has turned orange with age. It is native to Southern Europe and North Africa.

Amanita Persicina

While taller than *Amanita muscaria*, this mushroom species has been called "peach-colored fly agaric". It's normally mistaken for fly agaric in its older life phase, when the mushroom's cap turns orange or yellow, representing *Amanita muscaria* variants like yellow *guessowii* (*formosa*).

Amanita Parcivolvata

With less distinctive warts and a less prominent stem, this mushroom looks similar to *Amanita muscaria* due to its red color and whitish warts. Commonly found throughout the southeastern parts of the US, it has also been called the "Ringless False Fly Agaric" or "False Caesars's Mushroom". It differs by its pileal striations and by the absence of an annulus. This mushroom is edible, yet easy to misidentify.

There are likely a number of other lookalikes that could be potentially mistaken for Amanita muscaria, in addition to those that I have discussed here. Certain mushrooms are deadly, like the *Amanita virosa,* also known as the "Destroying Angel". This mushroom causes kidney or liver dysfunction, with symptoms starting between 6 and 24 hours, and is responsible for over 90% of fatal poisonings with mushrooms (Wennig et al., 2020).

There are also different variations of *Amanita muscaria* which you may be able to use, and you might want to learn more about. It's estimated that there are 1.5 million species in the fungi kingdom, with less than 10% of them already discovered, so you can find anything out there. You need to be very cautious when foraging for mushrooms, and when in doubt, it's better to discard them!

Drying Process

The first step is finding the mushroom, It is recommended that you collect fresh specimens, as this will provide you with high levels of ibotenic acid that can be converted into high levels of muscimol. However, they should be processed as soon as possible after being collected. Drying is one of the more commonly used methods for decarboxylating ibotenic acid to muscimol, but remember, the conversion won't happen if you dry your batch below 165°F (72°C), but it's still a precautionary measurement against neurotoxins. For decarboxylation, I dry them at 190°F (87°C).

This method allows for significant changes to occur in the concentration of chemicals and compounds found in fly agaric, and it will impact how these chemicals could potentially affect you. However, the results of drying will vary depending on the size of the *Amanita muscaria* cap that you are using, as well as its unique composition. You should never wash your mushroom caps before drying them; simply use a brush to remove dirt gently. The section that follows will provide you with a brief explanation of these techniques.

Above a Heat Source

You could hang your mushrooms above a heat source like a cooking top, the oven, or even a fireplace. You will know it's ready when it becomes crispy.

Oven

Oven drying can be tricky as the mushroom will be at risk of burning, especially if your oven's ventilation isn't very good. Something practical could be lifting the mushrooms away from the base with a wide steel grill or similar and leaving the oven partially open. The optimal temperature for the oven to preserve our batch is between 109 to 131°F (45 to 55°C).

Dehydrator

A dehydrator is considered one of the easiest and most effective methods. Once dried, allow the dried mushrooms to cool in a jar, and then dry them again the next day—preferably with a dehydrator—as they can easily absorb moisture.

Sunlight

If you are going to use direct sunlight as a drying method, keep in mind that UV radiation degrades the ibotenic acid to harmless muscazone. This explains why some people expose the final dried specimens to direct sunlight. I know someone who places his *Amanita muscaria* tea in direct sunlight as a final precautionary measure against the remaining ibotenic acid.

Storing

Once dried, you need to be able to store your *Amanita muscaria* mushrooms safely so that you can still use them during the months when they don't grow. When correctly dried and stored, the dried mushrooms can last for up to six months in the fridge and up to a year in a cool dark place. It's important that you keep the mushrooms away from moisture and sunlight as they become quite sensitive to the elements when dried. There are a number of ways to store dried mushrooms.

Main Ways to Store Dried Amanita Muscaria

The equipment that you need to store your mushrooms will depend on your method of storage. Some of the common equipment used include:

- Glass canning jars that can be placed in the fridge or freezer, preferably with a screw-on lid that fits securely.

- Airtight containers that can be stored in the fridge, freezer, or cupboard.

- Resealable bags or vacuum-sealable bags that are safe to freeze.

- Oxygen-absorbing packets, especially if you are storing your mushrooms at room temperature. They aren't necessary, but they are useful because of their ability to absorb the oxygen in the container that triggers the deterioration of food.

You can choose your equipment based on any of the storage methods below.

Refrigerator or Freezer

Using either an airtight container, glass jar, or resealable freezer bag, place your dried mushrooms inside. Carefully squeeze all the air out if you are using a plastic bag, screw on the lid tightly if using a jar, or carefully seal the container. Then, label the chosen container with the name of the contents, the date they were dried, and the date that they were put into storage. Place them into the fridge but keep them away from moisture-laden items like fresh fruit and vegetables. You can store your mushrooms like this for up to 6 months in the fridge and 12 months in the freezer.

Room Temperature

Using the same method above, you will carefully place the dried mushrooms in their new container—sealing it properly by carefully squeezing all the air from the packet, vacuum sealing it, or securing the jar or container—and then label it appropriately. The mushrooms should then be placed in a cool, dry place that prevents them from coming into contact with direct sunlight and moisture. This may be a kitchen cupboard, food pantry, or any other place fitting these specifications.

Curing

You can cure the Amanita muscaria mushrooms by leaving them to ferment in vacuum-sealable packaging. Place the carefully sealed package in a dark place in your home (where it won't come into contact with sunlight or moisture) at 46.4 to 53.6°F (8 to 12°C) for 2 to 3 months. Curing them may allow the mushroom's properties to last for up to a year.

The storage method that you choose will depend on what you have available to you, your environment, and the method that you are comfortable with. Storage becomes extremely helpful during the months when you cannot find *Amanita muscaria* in the wild but would still like to carry on microdosing.

Key Takeaways

- Correctly identifying and hunting your own *Amanita muscaria* is a fulfilling experience.

- Learning how to identify this mushroom correctly is important.

- While it isn't easy to mistake it for another mushroom, learning about its key characteristics will decrease your risk of mistaking it for one of the other *Amanita* species.

- Your mushrooms should be processed as soon as possible after collection.

- The mushroom is thoroughly dried when it becomes crispy.

- Once dried, it's important that you store your mushroom correctly in a dark, cool and dry place, properly sealed, so that it lasts and keeps its potency level.

- Storage is helpful during the time of year when you cannot find this mushroom growing in your local environment.

Learning how to hunt, dry, and preserve your *Amanita muscaria* is your final step to learning how to microdose as a beginner. It can be a fulfilling activity, but it's normal to feel unsure about hunting this mushroom on your own at first. Don't be afraid to ask for help from experienced mushroom hunters. You now have the information necessary to start your journey to microdosing with *Amanita muscaria*.

Conclusion

Microdosing with *Amanita muscaria* may seem intimidating at first, but I have broken down and explained the key information that you need to reap its benefits successfully. And this unique, yet iconic, mushroom has many—when properly prepared. Remember, you need to put in the work to use this mushroom safely and you have to respect that it can cause adverse effects when incorrectly used.

That's why I wrote this book. As someone who struggles with chronic pain because of an inflammatory condition, I understand that while this mushroom can't cure it; it provides me with some relief and the rest that I need to be able to enjoy my life more. I wish I could say that microdosing with *Amanita muscaria* completely eclipsed my symptoms, but that would not be completely honest. My mission with this manual was to share my knowledge and experience to educate and give hope to those with similar struggles who want to live their lives and have the opportunity to improve their overall well-being.

By learning about *Amanita muscaria*, you now know that this emblematic mushroom is made up of a number of complex chemicals. And one of these chemicals can be particularly harmful if not converted into a safer, more beneficial form of the compound. By looking at the different types of evidence and studies available, you could see that even though everyone has a unique reaction to this mushroom, it really can improve sleep, reduce and manage pain, and even improve your well-being, regardless of whether you have a pre-existing condition you are hoping to manage better.

By learning about how *Amanita muscaria* works, you now know that this mushroom is made up of a number of complex chemicals that can be harmful until they are converted into a safer, more beneficial form of that compound. By looking at the different types of evidence and studies available, you could see that even though everyone has a unique reaction to this mushroom, it really can improve sleep, reduce and manage pain, and even improve your well-being, regardless of whether you have a pre-existing condition you are hoping to better manage.

But there isn't a universal dosage. Microdosing is unique to everyone because of how your body is and how it's affected by each different batch of fly agaric. Each cap, regardless of its size, is also composed of different levels of ibotenic acid and muscimol. That's one of the reasons why you need to start with low doses. This isn't a race, and the possible benefits are worth the time it takes to figure out what form of microdosing works best for you.

It's actually quite amazing that a mushroom commonly called "fly agaric" has such unique potential in terms of its medicinal properties. We may not have much empirical evidence to support what we currently know, but the experiences of those who use *Amanita muscaria* to microdose have started inspiring others to pursue the possibility of this mushroom being able to improve their mental and physical well-being. Its rise in popularity has also started getting attention from researchers.

However, just like regular prescription medication, it can have side effects. That's why respecting this mushroom is an important part of safely using it. Understanding the possible common and adverse side effects also allows you to understand how you could possibly react after taking your first dose. This is key to helping you physically and mentally prepare to microdose for the first time. Additionally, it sheds some light on the reports of mushroom poisoning cases that have occurred.

Preparing properly can help you feel more confident about identifying and hunting *Amanita muscaria* in your local environment. You could buy it online, but mushroom foraging—when done correctly—can be a fulfilling practice. It helps you appreciate this mushroom and the nature that it grows in. This appreciation is carried through to the drying and storage processes, key activities to preparing for the months when you can't find fly agaric in nature.

You have the opportunity to take action and learn about something that could potentially make a big difference in your life. Even though this book provides you with only an overview of the most important information, you can still do extra research, join an online microdosing forum, and speak with others who have achieved the benefits that I have discussed throughout this book.

Microdosing won't look the same for everyone, but that's

one of the reasons why it's so great. You can make it fit your needs and lifestyle in a way that helps you maximize its benefits. So, take what you have learned from this book and decide for yourself whether microdosing with *Amanita muscaria* is something that **you** want to pursue for your health and well-being.

Bonus

Your journey starts here

One of the best practices when microdosing is to keep a journal to track your journey and find out what is working and what isn't working, so you can adjust. Remember, the form of consumption will alter the results and the slightest change in the intake can make the whole experience different. When microdosing with Amanita muscaria, it is advised to start small and adjust with small increases, dropping back the dosage weight when needed.

I recommend you start journaling before you even start microdosing, so you can have a reference on how you were feeling before starting. And try to keep objective and be always honest.

Notes for the daily journal:

- If you have had a break or interrupted the microdosing course, include the date of the last time you took it in "Last Intake".

- BOD stands for "Beginning of Day".

- EOD stands for "End of Day".

- In "Day" include both the day of the week and the day of the month.

- Fill in the drawn boxes with a scale that goes from one to ten, being zero null effect. You can do it later in the day but try to keep doing it at a regular time.

- The reflection/observations section can be completed at the end of the day, or perhaps the next day. It can include changes in your thoughts, behavior, and others.

- The daily benefit score goes from 1 to 100, being the total sum of the factors analyzed on that day.

Notes for the monthly overview:

- The first graph is intended to illustrate the monthly trend of the overall benefit from your microdosing journey. You will need the daily score tracking for at least a month.

- The rest of the graphs can be personalized, you might want to illustrate your monthly trend of creativity, sleep, or calmness to reflect your anxiety levels. So, feel free to use it at your convenience.

- The graphs are made following the monthly timeframe, but feel free to increase or decrease the counting days.

You can download the journal by scanning the next QR code:

The journal is also available for purchase (200 pages):

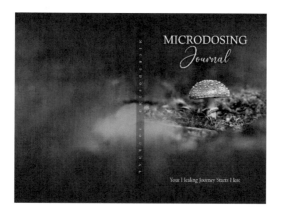

"Microdosing Journal: Amanita Muscaria (Fly agaric) Version. Your healing starts here"

Journal

One of the best practices when microdosing with Amanita muscaria is keeping a journal to track your journey and find out what is working and what isn't working, so you can adjust. Remember, the form of consumption will alter the results and the slightest change in the intake can make the whole experience different. When microdosing with Amanita muscaria, it is advised to start small and adjust with small increases, dropping back the dosage weight when needed.

I recommend you start journaling one or a couple of days before you even start microdosing, so you can have a reference on how you were feeling before starting. And try to keep objective and be always honest.

Notes for the daily journal:

- If you have had a break or interrupted the microdosing course, include the date of the last time you took it in "Last Intake".
- BOD stands for "Beginning of Day".
- EOD stands for "End of Day".
- In "Day" include both the day of the week and the day of the month.
- Fill in the drawn boxes with a scale that goes from one to ten, being zero null effect. You can do it later in the day but try to keep doing it at a regular time.
- The reflection/observations section can be completed at the end of the day, or perhaps the next day. It can include changes in your thoughts, behavior, and others.
- The daily benefit score goes from 1 to 100, being the total sum of the factors analyzed on that day.

Notes for the monthly overview:

- The first graph is intended to illustrate the monthly trend of the overall benefit from your microdosing journey. You will need the daily score tracking for at least a whole month.
- The rest of the graphs can be personalized, you might want to illustrate your monthly trend of creativity, sleep quality, or calmness to reflect your anxiety levels. So, feel free to use it at your convenience.
- The graphs are made following the monthly timeframe, but again feel free to increase or decrease the counting days.

JOURNAL EXAMPLE

DAY/TIME	DOSE	FORM	LAST INTAKE
Sat 24th Dec, 9am	0.3g	Dry	Thur 22th Dec, 7am

GOALS/INTENTIONS *I would love to stop fear from holding me back. I want to enjoy exercising this evening, as I am not very motivated lately…*

FEELINGS BOD *I feel like having more self-compassion for myself than the previous weeks, I woke up at 8:45 am and I am not guilty of it.*

MOOD	9	NOTES	
VITALITY	8	NOTES	
CALMNESS	9	NOTES	My panic attacks are gone.
CONCENTRATION	8	NOTES	Less procrastination
CREATIVITY	7	NOTES	
ENERGY LEVELS	8	NOTES	
RELATIONAL SKILLS	7	NOTES	
SENSES	6	NOTES	
SLEEP	10	NOTES	I fell asleep really fast and I didn't wake up until the alarm clock sounded.
GRATITUDE	8	NOTES	
DAILY BENEFIT SCORE	80	NOTES	

JOURNAL EXAMPLE

EFFECTS ON AILMENTS

My upper spine doesn't hurt as much today.

NEGATIVE EFFECTS

I felt a little bit nervous this morning.

SIDE EFFECTS (AND SEVERITY)

I didn't have a lot of appetite for breakfast, perhaps I waited too. long

FEELINGS EOD

I feel strong and proud of myself. I also feel inspired. I am kind of connecting with my inner child

REFLECTION/OBSERVATIONS

I went exercising and it was raining, and I didn't care :) And I feel I am forgiving myself, while more connected

Monthly Overview Example

Overall Benefits Analyzer Example

Mood Analyzer Example

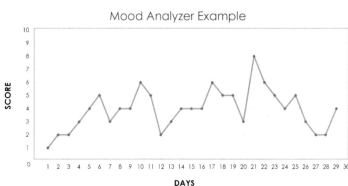

Clamness Analyzer (Inverted anxiety) Example

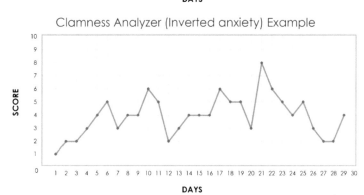

DAY/TIME	DOSE	FORM	LAST INTAKE

GOALS/INTENTIONS

FEELINGS BOD

EFFECTS ON AILMENTS

NEGATIVE EFFECTS

MOOD	☐	NOTE
VITALITY	☐	NOTE
CALMNESS	☐	NOTE
CONCENTRATION	☐	NOTE
CREATIVITY	☐	NOTE
ENERGY LEVELS	☐	NOTE
RELATIONAL SKILLS	☐	NOTE
SENSES	☐	NOTE
SLEEP	☐	NOTE
GRATITUDE	☐	NOTE
DAILY BENEFIT SCORE	☐	NOTE

SIDE EFFECTS (AND SEVERITY)

FEELINGS EOD

REFLECTION/OBSERVATIONS

Monthly Overview

Overall Benefits Analyzer

SCORE / DAYS

Analyzer

SCORE / DAYS

Analyzer

SCORE / DAYS

Monthly Overview

Analyzer

SCORE / DAYS

Analyzer

SCORE / DAYS

Analyzer

SCORE / DAYS

Dear Reader

I want to personally thank you for choosing this book from among dozens out there, for acquiring an authorized copy of it and supporting my work, and for making it all the way to the end.

If you liked the content, please consider posting a review or rating on Amazon, it would mean a lot to me and it would help others benefit from my work. It is also the best way to support independent writers like myself.

Thank you.

Amazon US   Amazon UK

You can use your respective Amazon market if you don't live in the UK or US.

References

Amanita muscaria guide: Effects, common uses, safety. (2022, January 14). *Reality Sandwich.* realitysandwich.com/amanita-muscaria-guide-effects-uses-safety/

Amanita muscaria vs magic mushrooms: Two stark differences. (2022, September 4). Psilo Mart. psilomart.com/blogs/articles/amanita-muscaria-vs-magic-mushrooms-effects-legality

Biziulevičius, G. A., and Vaitkuvienė, A. (2007). Taking advantage of the experience in ethnomedicinal use of mushrooms: Anti-inflammatory and related pharmacological activities of fly agaric (*Amanita muscaria*) ethanolic extract deserve a modern evaluation. *Medical Hypotheses*, 69(4), 946–947. doi.org/10.1016/j.mehy.2007.01.025

Blackwell, M. (2011). The Fungi: 1, 2, 3...5.1 million species? *American Journal of Botany*, 98(3), 426–438. doi.org/10.3732/ajb.1000298

Boskey, E. (2021). *What in vitro means in research studies.* Very Well Health. verywellhealth.com/what-is-in-vitro-biological-3132872

Britannica. (2022). Drugs affecting muscle: Muscarine. In *Encyclopædia Britannica.*

britannica.com/science/drug-chemical-agent/Drugs-affecting-muscle#ref797202

Buschfunkistan. (2019). Fly agaric-Ingredients, effects, and preparation (German w/ English subtitles) [YouTube Video]. In *YouTube.* youtube.com/watch?v=PhmpvGfYEGY

Çağdaş Yıldırım, Gulhan Kurtoglu, Gullu Ercan Haydar, and Ayhan Ozhasenekler. (2016, June 14). Mushroom Poisoning with Symptoms of Pantherina Syndrome: A Case Report. ResearchGate; *Journal of Emergency Medicine Case Reports.* researchgate.net/publication/303979941_Mus hroom_Poisoning_with_Symptoms_of_Panthe rina_Syndrome_A_Case_Report

Davis, S. (2022, October 19). *How to store dried mushrooms?* Top Food Storage Reviews. topfoodstoragereviews.com/how-to-store-dried-mushrooms/

Dutta, S. S. (2020, July 23). What are NMDA receptors? *News-Medical.* news-medical.net/life-sciences/What-are-NMDA-Receptors.aspx

Feeney, K. (2010). Revisiting Wasson's soma: Exploring the effects of preparation on the chemistry of Amanita muscaria. pdf. *Journal of Psychoactive Drugs,* 42(4), 499–506. doi.org/http://dx.doi.org/10.1080/02791072.2 010.10400712

Fletcher, J. (2020, July 13). What causes swelling, and is it serious? *Medical News Today*. medicalnewstoday.com/articles/swelling

Frost's Amanita (Amanita frostiana). (2014). JungleDragon. jungledragon.com/specie/25263/frosts_amanit a.html

Gamma-Aminobutyric Acid (GABA): What it is, function and benefits. (2022). Cleveland Clinic. my.clevelandclinic.org/health/articles/22857- gamma-aminobutyric-acid-gaba

Global Drug Survey 2017. (2017). Global Drug Survey. globaldrugsurvey.com/past-findings/gds2017- launch/results-released/

Gordon, J., and Bradford, A. (2022, February 8). *Empirical evidence: A definition*. Live Science. livescience.com/21456-empirical-evidence-a- definition.html#

Gruska, J. (2020, November 13). *Amanita muscaria: the science and use of the Fly agaric mushroom*. Medium. medium.com/@jonasgruska/amanita- muscaria-the-science-and-practice-of-the-fly- agaric-mushroom-587893d4bfe2

Hicks, A. (2022, January 6). *Amanita muscaria: Old World Magic Mushrooms. Cannadelics*. cannadelics.com/2022/01/06/amanita- muscaria-the-most-misunderstood-magic- mushroom/

Holland, K. (2020, February 5). *What You Should Know About Neuropathic Pain*. Healthline; Healthline Media. healthline.com/health/neuropathic-pain

How to make Amanita tea. (2015). The Amanita Forum. amanitaforum.com/amanita-tea-lemon-tek

Impact of migraine. (2022, February 2). The Migraine Trust. migrainetrust.org/understand-migraine/impact-of-migraine/

insomniacnextdoor. (2020, February 8). *Can Amanita muscaria mushroom help with sleep?* Insomniac Next Door. insomniacnextdoor.com/can-amanita-muscaria-mushroom-help-with-sleep/

Johns Pool, J. (2021). *How common is migraine?* Migraine Statistics and Facts. migraine.com/migraine-statistics

Johnston, G. A. R., M. Chebib, Duke, R. K., Fernandez, S. P., Hanrahan, J. R., Hinton, T., and K.N. Mewett. (2022). Herbal Products and GABA Receptors. *Encyclopedia of Neuroscience*, 1095–1101. academia.edu/3733201/Herbal_Products_and_GABA_Receptors

Jones, C. (2011, September 7). *Fly Agaric (Amanita muscaria).* Ireland's Wildlife. irelandswildlife.com/fly-agaric-amanita-muscaria/

Jones, M. (2022, May 11). *The magic of microdosing: An essential guide to microdosing for healing, creativity, and connection.* Medium. medium.com/@miasjones888/the-magic-of-microdosing-an-essential-guide-to-microdosing-for-healing-creativity-connection-2039bfb139a2

Kandola, A. (2020, October 19). What to know about asthenia (weakness). Medicalnewstoday.com; *Medical News Today.* medicalnewstoday.com/articles/asthenia-weakness

Kondeva-Burdina, M., Voynova, M., Shkondrov, A., Aluani, D., Tzankova, V., and Krasteva, I. (2019). Effects of Amanita muscaria extract on different in vitro neurotoxicity models at sub-cellular and cellular levels. *Food and Chemical Toxicology, 132,* 110687. doi.org/10.1016/j.fct.2019.110687

Krogsgaard-Larsen, P. (2018). THIP/Gaboxadol, a Unique GABA Agonist. Reference Module in *Biomedical Sciences.* doi.org/10.1016/b978-0-12-801238-3.97290-8

Krogsgaard-Larsen, P., Ebert, B., Lund, T., Bräuner-Osborne, H., Sløk, F., Johansen, T., Brehm, L., and Madsen, U. (1996). Design of excitatory amino acid receptor agonists, partial agonists and antagonists: ibotenic acid as a key lead structure. *European Journal of Medicinal*

Chemistry, 31(7-8), 515–537. doi.org/10.1016/0223-5234(96)89549-3

Krogsgaard-Larsen, P., Frølund, B., Liljefors, T., and Ebert, B. (2004). GABAA agonists and partial agonists: THIP (Gaboxadol) as a non-opioid analgesic and a novel type of hypnotic. *Biochemical Pharmacology*, 68(8), 1573–1580. doi.org/10.1016/j.bcp.2004.06.040

Krogsgaard-Larsen, P., Nilsson, L., Boll, P. M., Hope, H., Christensen, A., and Schroll, G. (1977). Muscimol Analogues. II. Synthesis of Some Bicyclic 3-Isoxazolol Zwitterions. *Acta Chemica Scandinavica*, 31b, 584–588. doi.org/10.3891/acta.chem.scand.31b-0584

Levy, R. (2001). Lidocaine and muscimol microinjections in subthalamic nucleus reverse parkinsonian symptoms. *Brain*, 124(10), 2105–2118. doi.org/10.1093/brain/124.10.2105

Lewis, T. (2014, December 12). *"Magic" mushrooms in royal garden: What is Fly Agaric?* Live Science. livescience.com/49118-magic-mushrooms-royal-gardens.html

Masha, B. (2022). *Microdosing with Amanita Muscaria*. Simon and Schuster.

Matsumoto, T., Trueb, W., Gwinner, R., and Eugster, C. H. (1969). Isolierung von (?)-R-4-Hydroxy-pyrrolidon-(2) und einigen weiteren Verbindungen aus Amanita muscaria. 31.

Mitteilung ber Inhaltsstoffe von Fliegenpilzen. *Helvetica Chimica Acta,* 52(3), 716–720. doi.org/10.1002/hlca.19690520320

Mayo Clinic. (2021a). *Arthritis–Symptoms and causes.* Mayo Clinic; mayoclinic.org/diseases-conditions/arthritis/symptoms-causes/syc-20350772

Mayo Clinic. (2021b). *Common cold–Symptoms and causes.* Mayo Clinic; mayoclinic.org/diseases-conditions/common-cold/symptoms-causes/syc-20351605

Mayo Clinic. (2021c). *Migraine–Symptoms and causes.* Mayo Clinic; mayoclinic.org/diseases-conditions/migraine-headache/symptoms-causes/syc-20360201

Mayo Clinic. (2021d). *Musculoskeletal Pain: Types, Causes, Symptoms and Treatment.* Cleveland Clinic. my.clevelandclinic.org/health/diseases/14526-musculoskeletal-pain

Mayo Clinic. (2021e). *Rheumatoid arthritis–Symptoms and causes.* Mayo Clinic; mayoclinic.org/diseases-conditions/rheumatoid-arthritis/symptoms-causes/syc-20353648

Mayo Clinic. (2022a). *Ankylosing spondylitis–Symptoms and causes.* Mayo Clinic;

mayoclinic.org/diseases-conditions/ankylosing-spondylitis/symptoms-causes/syc-20354808

Mayo Clinic. (2022b). *Psoriasis–Symptoms and causes*. Mayo Clinic; mayoclinic.org/diseases-conditions/psoriasis/symptoms-causes/syc-20355840

Merriam-Webster. (n.d.-a). Anecdotal evidence. In the *Merriam-Webster Dictionary*. Retrieved November 6, 2022, from merriam-webster.com/dictionary/anecdotal%20evidence

Merriam-Webster. (n.d.-b). Asthenia. In the *Merriam-Webster Dictionary*. Retrieved November 12, 2022, from merriam-webster.com/dictionary/asthenia

Merriam-Webster. (n.d.-c). Decarboxylation. In the *Merriam-Webster Dictionary*. Retrieved November 6, 2022, from merriam-webster.com/dictionary/decarboxylation

Merriam-Webster. (n.d.-d). Symbiotic. In the *Merriam-Webster Dictionary*. Retrieved November 7, 2022, from merriam-webster.com/dictionary/symbiotic

Merriam-Webster. (2017). Analgesic. In the *Merriam-Webster Dictionary*. merriam-webster.com/dictionary/analgesic

Merriam-Webster. (2019). Anxiolytic. In the *Merriam-Webster Dictionary*. merriam-webster.com/dictionary/anxiolytic

Merriam-Webster. (2022a). Goiter. In the *Merriam-Webster Dictionary*. merriam-webster.com/dictionary/goiter

Merriam-Webster. (2022b). Hypertension. In the *Merriam-Webster Dictionary*. merriam-webster.com/dictionary/hypertension

Nelson, R. (2021a, November 3). *The Fly Agaric is toxic AND edible–The basic science*. Stone Age Man. stoneageman.com/the-fly-agaric-is-poisonous-and-edible/

Nelson, R. (2021b, December 13). *The Fly Agaric*. Untamed Science. untamedscience.com/biodiversity/fly-agaric/

NIAMS. (2017, April 21). *Autoimmune Diseases*. National Institute of Arthritis and Musculoskeletal and Skin Diseases. niams.nih.gov/health-topics/autoimmune-diseases

Nielsen, E. Ø., Schousboe, A., Hansen, S. H., and Krogsgaard-Larsen, P. (1985). Excitatory Amino Acids: Studies on the Biochemical and Chemical Stability of Ibotenic Acid and Related Compounds. *Journal of Neurochemistry*, 45(3), 725–731. doi.org/10.1111/j.1471-4159.1985.tb04052.x ninakhokhlova49. (2022, January 27). *Amanita Muscaria Microdosing.* Muscaria.store. muscaria.store/post/amanita-muscaria-microdosing

Pahapill, P. A., Levy, R., Dostrovsky, J. O., Davis, K. D., Rezai, A. R., Tasker, R. R., and Lozano, A. M. (1999). Tremor arrest with thalamic microinjections of muscimol in patients with essential tremor. *Annals of Neurology,* 46(2), 249–252. doi.org/3.0.co;2-c">10.1002/1531-8249(199908)46:2<249::aid-ana15>3.0.co;2-c

Ponieman, N. (2022, October 6). *This legal psychoactive mushroom reduces stress and pain and encourages longevity, expert says.* Benzinga. benzinga.com/markets/cannabis/21/12/20669337/this-legal-psychoactive-mushroom-reduces-stress-and-pain-and-encourages-longevity-expert-says

Prevalence of migraines–How common are migraines? (2016). The Migraine Institute. themigraineinstitute.com/migraine-overview/prevalence-of-migraines/

Price, S. (2022, April 27). *Amanita muscaria extract shows immune priming activity.* Psychedelic Health. psychedelichealth.co.uk/2022/04/27/amanita-muscaria-extract-shows-immune-priming-activity/

Puschner, B. (2018). Mushroom toxins: Mechanism of action. *Veterinary Toxicology (Third Edition).* Science Direct. doi.org/sciencedirect.com/topics/agricultural-and-biological-sciences/muscarine

Ruthes, A. C., Carbonero, E. R., Córdova, M. M., Baggio, C. H., Sassaki, G. L., Gorin, P. A. J., Santos, A. R. S., and Iacomini, M. (2013). Fucomannogalactan and glucan from mushroom Amanita muscaria: Structure and inflammatory pain inhibition. *Carbohydrate Polymers,* 98(1), 761–769. doi.org/10.1016/j.carbpol.2013.06.061

SalviaSeeker. (2022). *Amanita–Ibotenic acid to muscimol acceleration.* Entheogen Network. entheogen-network.com/forums/viewtopic.php?f=9&t=10943

Satora, L., Pach, D., Butryn, B., Hydzik, P., and Balicka-Ślusarczyk, B. (2005). Fly agaric (Amanita muscaria) poisoning, case report and review. *Toxicon,* 45(7), 941–943. doi.org/10.1016/j.toxicon.2005.01.005

Schwartzberg, L., and Monroe, M. (2019). Fantastic Fungi [Video]. In *Netflix.*

The seeker's guide to Amanita muscaria. (2019). EntheoNation. entheonation.com/amanita-muscaria-guide/#tve-jump-17651d158ae

Shroomery Message Board. (2014, October 17). *Amanita Muscaria: how to (work in progress)—The psychedelic experience.* Shroomery. shroomery.org/forums/showflat.php/Number/ 20715953/fpart/all

Sylvia. (2017, December 14). *Facts and benefits of aga (Fly Agaric).* Health Benefits Times. healthbenefitstimes.com/aga-fly-agaric/

Tamminga, C. A., Neophytides, A., Chase, T. N., and Frohman, L. A. (1978). Stimulation of prolactin and growth hormone secretion by muscimol, a γ-Aminobutyric acid agonist*. *The Journal of Clinical Endocrinology and Metabolism*, 47(6), 1348–1351. doi.org/10.1210/jcem-47-6-1348

TrippyWiki. (2021, April 4). *Amanita muscaria: Effects, dosage, how to take it and more.* TrippyWiki. trippywiki.com/amanita-muscaria/#microdosing

Tsonuda, K., Inoue, N., Aoyagi, Y., and Sugahara, T. (1993). Change in ibotenic acid and muscimol contents in Amanita muscaria during drying, storing or cooking. *Food Hygiene and Safety Science (Shokuhin Eiseigaku Zasshi)*, 34(2), 153-160_1. doi.org/10.3358/shokueishi.34.153

Tsujikawa, K., Mohri, H., Kuwayama, K., Miyaguchi, H., Iwata, Y., Gohda, A., Fukushima, S., Inoue, H., and Kishi, T. (2006). Analysis of hallucinogenic constituents in Amanita mushrooms circulated in Japan. *Forensic Science International,* 164(2-

3), 172–178. doi.org/10.1016/j.forsciint.2006.01.004

The ultimate guide to Amanita muscaria. (2021, May 18). Third Wave. thethirdwave.co/psychedelics/amanita-muscaria/

US20140004084A1–Method for producing muscimol and/or reducing ibotenic acid from amanita tissue. (2013, July 2). Google Patents. patents.google.com/patent/US20140004084

Wennig, R., Eyer, F., Schaper, A., Zilker, T., & Andresen-Streichert, H. (2020). Mushroom Poisoning. *Deutsches Ärzteblatt International.* doi.org/10.3238/arztebl.2020.0701

Why and how to dry Amanita muscaria. (2021, December 17). Amanita Dreamer. amanitadreamer.net/post/grow-your-blog-community

Wikipedia Contributors. (2020, September 11). *Muscazone.* Wikipedia; Wikimedia Foundation. en.wikipedia.org/wiki/Muscazone

Wikipedia Contributors. (2022a, October 7). *Decarboxylation.* Wikipedia; Wikimedia Foundation. en.wikipedia.org/wiki/Decarboxylation

Wikipedia Contributors. (2022, June 27). Amanita frostiana. Wikipedia; Wikimedia Foundation. en.wikipedia.org/wiki/Amanita_frostiana

Wikipedia Contributors. (2022b, November 4). *Amanita muscaria*. Wikipedia; Wikimedia Foundation. en.wikipedia.org/wiki/Amanita_muscaria#Toxicity

Wikipedia Contributors. (2022, October 30). *Amanita phalloides*. Wikipedia; Wikimedia Foundation. en.wikipedia.org/wiki/Amanita_phalloides

Wilensky, A. E., Schafe, G. E., Kristensen, M. P., and LeDoux, J. E. (2006). Rethinking the Fear Circuit: The Central Nucleus of the Amygdala Is Required for the Acquisition, Consolidation, and Expression of Pavlovian Fear Conditioning. *Journal of Neuroscience*, 26(48), 12387–12396. doi.org/10.1523/jneurosci.4316-06.2006

Zhang, X., and Paule, M. G. (2010a). In Vivo Systems: Animal Models of Neurodegeneration*. *Comprehensive Toxicology*, 399–413. doi.org/10.1016/b978-0-08-046884-6.01324-5

Zhang, X., and Paule, M. G. (2010b). Nervous system and behavioral toxicology: Ibotenic Acid. *Comprehensive Toxicology*, 13.23.3.3.2(ii)(c). doi.org/sciencedirect.com/topics/pharmacology-toxicology-and-pharmaceutical-science/ibotenic-acid

Bergo, A. (2021, October 2). *Japanese amanita muscaria mushroom pickles (fermented)*. Forager Chef. foragerchef.com/muscaria-pickles/

In inima Transilvaniei. (2022, October 27). *Tinctura de amanita muscaria impotriva durerilor de sciatica*. [Video]. YouTube. youtube.com/watch?v=aH2-5FaJU2c

Kathryn, E. (2020, August 7). *Amanita muscaria (fly agaric) tincture*. [Video]. YouTube. youtube.com/watch?v=FctCM44caRA

You don't eat muscaria, do you? (or, how to cook the "Christmas" mushroom). (2021, November 5). Wild Woman Kitchen. wildwomankitchen.com/you-dont-cook-muscaria-do-you-or-how-to-cook-the-christmas-mushroom/

Image References

macro.viewpoint. (n.d.). *Fly agaric mushroom Stock image 2073704996.* Shutterstock. shutterstock.com/es/image-photo/macro-single-red-fly-agaric-mushroom-2073704996

942784. (2015). Toadstool mushroom Fall Amanita [JPG Image]. In *Pixabay*. pixabay.com/photos/toadstool-mushroom-fall-1006896/

Skorchanov. (2020). Panther cap mushroom toadstool [JPG Image]. In *Pixabay*. pixabay.com/photos/panther-cap-mushroom-toadstool-5573495/

Viard, M. (2021). Death cap deadly poisonous Amanita phalloides [JPG Image]. In *iStock*. istockphoto.com/es/foto/death-capgm1300103653-392528636?phrase=amanita%20phalloides

WolfBlur. (2017). Toadstool red fly agaric umbrella [JPG Image]. In *Pixabay*. pixabay.com/photos/toadstool-red-fly-agaric-umbrella-2829356/

TShaKopy. (n.d.). *Agaric tincture Stock Image 2211923759.* Shutterstock. shutterstock.com/es/image-photo/fly-agaric-red-amber-glass-dropper-2211923759

Simol1407. (n.d.). *Dried pieces of Fly agaric Stock Image 2119844651.* Shutterstock. shutterstock.com:443/es/image-photo/dried-pieces-mushroom-fly-agaric-on-2119844651

Aquarius. (2014, April 1). *Amanita muscaria—create your own magic oil.* [Video]. YouTube. youtube.com/watch?v=3_90MLSTYAA